$2.50

D1106563

Plantation Patriot

by the same author

OCEAN PATHFINDER
A Biography of Matthew Fontaine Maury

Plantation Patriot

A Biography of Eliza Lucas Pinckney

Frances Leigh Williams

Illustrated with photographs and maps

Harcourt, Brace & World, Inc., New York

For my sister
Mary Mason Holt

Foreword

Eliza Lucas Pinckney (1723-1793) would have been a remarkable woman in any age. In the eighteenth century she was extraordinary. Forced by circumstances to manage three plantations at the age of sixteen, Eliza went on to be the first person in the American colonies to grow indigo successfully and to produce the dye, which was much in demand and thus brought great wealth to South Carolina in the decades before the American Revolution.

Eliza's thoughts and actions were often in advance of her times—as, for example, her refusal to accept either of two marriages arranged by her father because of her determination to marry a man of her own choice. In other ways she was very much of her own era. Like most people of the eighteenth century, she accepted the institution of slavery without question. She was deeply concerned for and dedicated to the welfare of her family's slaves, but her conscience was not aroused about the ownership and exploitation of other human beings. In considering this, we must remember that only the Quakers had raised significant protest against slavery at the time Eliza was managing her father's plantations. There is no evidence that she ever heard of those early denunciations of slavery. In 1777, Vermont adopted a state constitution that forbade slavery. In those years some of the farsighted fathers of the republic spoke out against slavery, but their convictions did not change the views of a great number of Americans. It was not until 1807 that the British Parliament passed a bill for the abolition of slave trade. More than a quarter of a century went by before England's Emancipation Act was passed in 1833. No one needs to be reminded how much longer it took for Americans officially to face the evils of slavery and end it in our own country.

The story of Eliza Lucas Pinckney's life is available to us in considerable detail because her letters, letter books in which she copied or abstracted letters she sent, and journals were saved from burning by a great-granddaughter, Eliza Lucas Rutledge. Unfortunately, no likeness of Eliza survives. If there was a portrait of her, and there probably was, it undoubtedly perished in the destruction of Belmont, her plantation home, about 1780, or in the fire that destroyed the Pinckneys' town house in Charleston in 1861. It is surmised that Eliza was a brunette because she chose dresses of a color becoming to a dark-haired girl. One of her gowns, now owned by the Charleston Museum, reveals that she was both slim and small of stature. Comments in letters also bear this out.

This book is based primarily on Eliza's letters and journals. I had the privilege of studying these at the South Carolina Historical Society, which owns them. Many of these letters are reproduced in the biography *Eliza Pinckney,* written in 1896 by her descendant, Harriott Horry Ravenel. I have quoted some of these letters and have made a few minor alterations in spelling to avoid distracting the modern reader with the individualism of eighteenth-century spelling. It might be added that, on the whole, Eliza spelled well and expressed herself clearly in a strong, angular handwriting. Another printed source of some of Eliza's writings is the *Journal and Letters of Eliza Lucas,* published in a limited edition in 1850 at Wormsloe, Georgia.

Invaluable as are these first-hand accounts by Eliza, they leave many gaps in information, especially in the matter of dates. To learn the military record of her father and that of his fellow officers, as well as facts about George Lucas's lieutenant governorship of Antigua and his death, a search of official records in the Public Record Office in London was necessary. Other needed facts have been secured from records in St. John's, Antigua, where the authorities have been most helpful to me.

Printed works by Eliza's contemporaries, newspapers and magazines of the time, histories, pamphlets, and scholarly journals have supplied further information and background material.

In trying to re-create a person so vitally alive as the young Eliza Lucas, I have taken the liberty of introducing a fictional character, Robert Leicester. I have done this because my study has convinced me that anyone as socially popular and attractive to men as Eliza had some romantic flurries in her life before she became engaged and married to Charles Pinckney. I have also invented Captain Duclos because there is evidence that someone familiar with indigo told Eliza how Nicholas Cromwell damaged the quality of her first cubes of dye. Similarly, Rhett Broughton, who reported the war news from London, is an imagined person, representative of the South Carolina gentlemen who came and went with frequency between Carolina and the mother country. Since careful search did not uncover the name of the man who served George Lucas as agent in Charles Town, I was obliged to give him a name—Samuel Millington. And finally, as Eliza rarely used Christian names in her letters and journals, I have devised them for her friends in Antigua, Miss Brambly and Miss Dunbar.

Also, Eliza's assistance at the Charles Town fire is a possibility but not a certainty. I have detailed these additions to recorded fact so that the reader may be assured that the historicity of the essential story of Eliza Lucas Pinckney has not been tampered with.

Eliza's story has long been known in South Carolina and

in her beloved Charles Town, which was renamed Charleston in 1783. Extremely valuable to me was a visit to Wappoo plantation, where the view from the site of the house was unchanged from Eliza's time. The Lucas dwelling no longer stands, but elsewhere in South Carolina I visited other houses of the period. I felt very close to Eliza as I walked over the Wappoo fields, where she planted her crops and achieved her success with indigo. I also endeavored to absorb the feeling of old Charleston through two visits to that historic city.

I wish to express appreciation to the following persons who have given me assistance in obtaining information for this book: The Permanent Secretary, Ministry of Home Affairs and Social Services, Antigua; Mrs. Phyllis Mayers, Librarian, Public Library, St. John's, Antigua; Mrs. Pendleton Powell Carmody, London, England; Dr. Edward Nelson MacConomy and Miss Mary Lil Latimer, Library of Congress, Washington; Mrs. Patricia Strickland and Mrs. Alma Deane MacConomy, Washington; Mrs. Mary B. Prior, Executive Secretary, South Carolina Historical Society, Charleston; Miss Helen G. McCormack, Curator, Gibbes Art Gallery, Charleston; Mrs. Jane Bell Gladding, Associate Professor of Chemistry and Dean of Women, Richmond Professional Institute, Richmond, Virginia; Thomas Pinckney, Richmond. Special acknowledgment is made of the encouragement to do this book that was given me by the late Josephine Pinckney, Charleston novelist.

I hope that through this book many more Americans will come to know of Eliza Lucas Pinckney, one of the great women of our nation's history.

Frances Leigh Williams

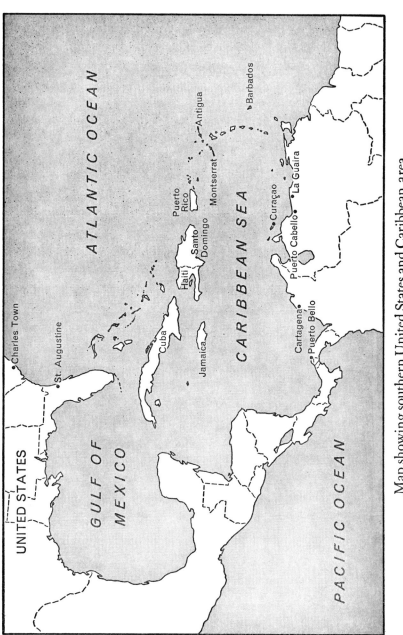

Map showing southern United States and Caribbean area

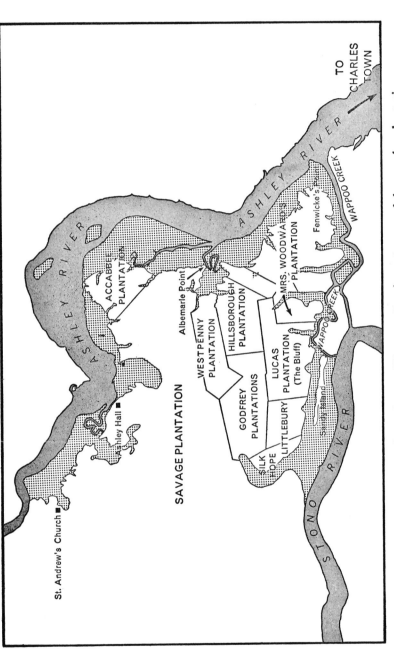

Map showing the Lucas plantation on Wappoo Creek and some of the nearby plantations

One

"Hurry, Eliza, the carriages are waiting at the door," Major George Lucas called to his daughter, who was coming down the hall toward him. "Run and see if your mother and Polly are ready."

"Yes, Papa," fifteen-year-old Eliza replied, her voice full of excitement. She could hardly believe the moment had finally come to leave their home in the tropical Caribbean island of Antigua and go to her father's plantations in South Carolina. She was bursting with curiosity as to what it would be like to live on the mainland in the American colonies. But there was no second for her to waste now on speculations. Eliza picked up her long hooped skirt and ran swiftly to her mother's room.

She automatically slowed her pace as she entered, for Mrs. Lucas had been ill for a long time. In the semidarkness of the shuttered room, Eliza could see her mother lying on the bed, a damp cloth over her eyes.

Bella, a tall, elderly Negro maid, signaled for silence, raising a finger to her lips. She spread the fingers of her other hand expressively to show that her mistress needed five minutes of rest.

Eliza nodded her head and went to the nursery next door, where she found her small sister, Polly, already dressed. The child's nurse was packing some last-minute things. "Quick,

Noni," Eliza said to the young Negress. "Take that portmanteau to the carriage. Papa is waiting for it. I'll go with Polly to the garden until Mama is ready. Then send for us right away."

Polly tugged impatiently at her sister's skirt.

"Wait a moment," Eliza said, "while I tie on my bonnet. Oh, I wish I had a smaller hat to travel in instead of this leghorn!"

She then took a firm clasp on little Polly's hand, for the child was noted for getting lost at just the wrong time. Laughing together, they went through a door that led to the garden.

It was very early in the morning, but the hot sun of the West Indies was already drying the dew on the luxuriant shrubs and vines in the Lucas garden. As the girls entered the walled area, a wave of perfume from tropical blooms wafted toward them. Overhead, a gannet flew lazily toward the harbor. The fish-eating bird was followed by a pair of bright-colored orioles. Tiny hummingbirds went busily from bloom to bloom. The garden was a riot of color—jasmine and stephanotis and lovely golden shower. Eliza plucked a scarlet hibiscus and tucked it over her ear.

Polly pouted. "Stop prettying up. I want a banana."

The two girls ran down the path made of crushed white shells. Eliza slowed up to give a good-by pat to the trunk of a mango tree as she passed it. The mango was a special pet of hers because it had long supplied her with fruit to make the family's favorite sweetmeat.

When they reached a heavily laden banana plant, Eliza stood on tiptoe and pulled a piece of the tropical fruit for her roly-poly sister. Polly was always hungry.

"Just think of the adventure we're going on, Polly. None of the family has ever stayed on the plantations in South

Carolina since Grandpa Lucas bought them in 1713. That's twenty-five years ago! And now Papa has inherited all three of them. He'll have more land there than any man has on this whole island."

Polly looked at her in disbelief. "Stop fibbing, Eliza, and making up such big tales. . . . Oh look, here comes Cully."

Cully was their butler-houseman, a dark-skinned man with alert eyes and snowy white hair. "Better run," he shouted.

The sisters dashed toward the front of the house, where their father's voice could be heard booming out their names. Eliza stopped in admiration when she saw her parents. Her handsome soldierly-looking father wore the uniform of his rank, a major in the army of His Majesty, George II of England. Even though Mrs. Lucas was pale and thin, they made a distinguished appearance together.

Suddenly Eliza was overcome with doubts. Was her mother strong enough to stand the sea voyage that lay ahead? Would getting away from the tropics cure her or would the trip prove a mistake? A longing for her two brothers swept over her. If only George and Tommy were going with them, she thought. But the boys had been sent to England to school.

"Eliza, you ride with your mother, and Bella also. Polly and her nurse will go in the carriage with me. The other servants are already on board the *Pretty Betsey*. Cully can ride on the carriage box with my driver." Major Lucas's voice rang with the authority of an officer whose commands were always obeyed.

Bella held a parasol over her mistress's head.

"I wonder when we shall be seeing this nicely laid out town again," remarked Mrs. Lucas plaintively to Eliza. Your father is so respected here in St. John's, as was his father before him. I question whether 'tis wise to go to this land where we will be strangers."

"Now, Mama, please do not fret about it. If the change to the cooler climate improves your health, I don't care if we never come back. Besides, Papa says you will find South Carolina's port city of Charles Town far more impressive than St. John's."

"Well, I would go anywhere to please your papa. He is convinced that it is the West Indies heat that has destroyed my vitality," replied Mrs. Lucas.

Bella was staring out over the harbor. Eliza followed her gaze and cried out, "Oh, Mama dear, look—there's the *Pretty Betsey* riding at anchor, waiting for us."

Disappointment clouded Mrs. Lucas's face. "I thought 'twould be a larger vessel," she said in a subdued voice.

Eliza tried to reassure her mother by reporting that her father had declared the one-hundred-ton sloop large enough to transport the family, house servants, and even a quantity of his sugar to sell in Charles Town.

They found a number of friends gathered to say good-by when they reached the wharf. Officers of the 38th Foot, South Staffordshire, Major Lucas's regiment, were on hand. "Gad, George," Eliza heard one of them say to her father, "stop worrying about the regiment. We can easily manage without you while you're on leave. These peace negotiations with Spain will keep everything quiet. We'll have no military action."

Eliza heard no more, for a ruddy-cheeked young officer bowed low to her. "Miss Eliza," he said, "allow me to make you a small gift for your journey." It was a box of candied ginger. As the ensign continued his farewells to her, Eliza noticed her father's good friend and immediate superior in the regiment, Lieutenant Colonel Valentine Morris, and Mr.

Brambly, a prominent merchant of St. John's. With them was Charles Dunbar, the controller of customs for the island.

Behind the men she spied her closest friends, Nellie Brambly and Pamela Dunbar. Both girls looked miserable. Eliza excused herself and slipped over to them.

"Eliza, what shall I do without you?" Nellie asked tearfully. "It was so lonely while you were in England at school, and here you are, going off so soon again. No one else is as much fun or has new ideas all the time the way you do. I shall miss you so terribly."

Pamela started to cry softly.

"Please don't cry, Pam. It's frightfully hard to leave you and my other Antigua friends. I don't know a soul in Carolina. But when Mama is better, we shall probably come back. Papa is not giving up his post here."

Then at last they were on board ship. The sloop's burly master, Captain Edward Evans, boomed out, "Major Lucas, your pardon, sir, but if you could tend to the comfort of your party, I'd best be gettin' *Pretty Betsey* under way afore the tide turns."

"Yes, yes, Captain. Proceed at once. Wouldn't wish to get stuck on the bar in a low tide."

Major Lucas called his wife's faithful maid, who had nursed her during her long illness. "Bella, your mistress must lie down promptly."

Bella nodded her instant agreement. She seldom wasted time on words.

As Mrs. Lucas was assisted toward the cabin, Eliza was torn between the desire to help her mother get settled and a longing to wave farewell to her friends still standing on the wharf. The problem was resolved for her when her mother declared, "Please, all of you leave me except Bella. I need to be quiet."

Wind-bronzed Captain Evans, standing in the aft part of the ship close to the helmsman, bellowed to men near the bow, "Weigh, boys." The winch creaked as four ebony-skinned sailors turned the capstan to haul in the anchor. The heavily muscled men sweated with their effort. Slowly the chain began to rattle up from the water.

Barefooted seamen had already raised the sails, and now, as the canvas filled with a fresh breeze, the tall mast creaked and groaned.

Polly asked Captain Evans in a scared voice, "Will that pole break?"

"No, lass," he replied. "That's the mast and 'tis strong. Look to the top. See the great pennant. Isn't it fine the way the wind blows it?"

But Polly was still uncertain and snuggled close to her sister for comfort.

Bells chimed somewhere in the sloop, and they were under way. Listening to the emerald-colored water slap rhythmically against the sides of the *Pretty Betsey,* Eliza felt a pang of homesickness. She wondered if she would ever come back to Antigua and the familiar, safe life she had known there, so carefree and happy. How she would miss the flowers she had herself grown, the gay parties at the Brambly and Dunbar homes, and, especially, the exciting young ensign who had so recently come out from England to join the 38th Regiment of Foot that had long been stationed in Antigua. How silly, she thought to herself, to have sad thoughts when starting out on an adventure! With that decision made, she stuck her pretty little pointed chin up in the air and began to plan all the things she would do once they reached South Carolina.

Eliza turned for a last look at the island of Antigua. Except for her years at school in London, she had never lived anywhere else. She loved the way the island rose sharply from the water and stood out in bold relief against the bright October sky. Overhead, there were great puffs of white clouds. The intense autumn heat of the West Indies was setting in for the day. Eliza daintily patted the perspiration from her forehead and did the same for Polly.

With her father, she leaned on the rail and gazed out over the deep violet-blue of the nearby water to the patches of green and turquoise near the shore. "Look, Papa," Eliza cried. "When the spray breaks on the beach, it is just the color of Mama's amethyst brooch."

Major Lucas smiled at her. "It makes me happy to have you love the beauty of nature, Eliza. It adds so much to the life of any man or woman. When we reach Carolina, we will study together the plants and flowers that we do not know." He leaned over to lift small Polly up on his shoulder. "Look at that little fishing vessel tacking back and forth to catch the wind to go into the harbor." To Eliza he added, "On this day in 1738 men do that just as they have for thousands of years."

A flight of pelicans flapped over the water in a long, solemn procession. The sun glinted on the silver of a flying fish as it leaped from the waves. Not far off, playful dolphin frolicked together.

"Soon we'll pass Sandy Island, and then we'll see the island of Montserrat off to the southwest. It makes a remarkable sight, with its jagged peaks rising from the water."

"That's where they make indigo," Eliza murmured.

"Yes. I wish we British knew as much about making indigo dye as they do in the French and Spanish possessions. We make a little, but we must buy great quantities for our weavers at home, and 'tis a shame that so much good English money goes to the French and Spanish for that precious blue dye."

Fair weather prevailed as long as they were in Caribbean waters. But once the *Pretty Betsey* sailed into the waters of the Atlantic, it was a different story. Mrs. Lucas and Polly were both seasick. Eliza was kept busy trying to make them comfortable and assuring Bella and Noni that the rough weather would not last.

Off the Florida coast the winds suddenly slackened, and the ship was becalmed for days. Captain Evans grumbled to Major Lucas, "This calm is enough to sicken a navigator's heart. By Jonah's whale, Major, 'tis good we're not at war with the Spaniards."

The captain pointed a stocky finger landward. "They've got a powerful fort with big cannon over there at St. Augustine. Those Spanish are spoiling to limber them up and shoot some Englishmen. I hope those ambassadors discussing peace manage to sign a treaty. I'd mightily hate for English troops to ever have to storm that St. Augustine fort."

One mid-November morning when Eliza waked, she heard bustling activity all over the *Pretty Betsey*. She dressed quickly and went on deck. There she found her father, who greeted her with good news. "Captain Evans tells me we are coming up by Morris Island, which lies to the south of Charles Town harbor."

Eagerly Eliza rushed across the deck for her first glimpse of this new land of which her father had told her so much. "Oh," she cried in disappointment, " 'tis such a low country —almost a dead level. Is it all sand, Papa? How will we raise fine crops?"

"No, no, my impatient one. Our land is back from the coast a few miles. I understand it is higher ground, and the fields are a sandy loam. This is only a coastal island." He added, "We are required to lie under the cannon of Fort Johnson until we have been examined and are permitted to land."

Eliza was puzzled and asked her father why this was necessary.

"The port doctor will come aboard and see if anyone has Siam distemper, guinea fever, or any contagious disease. Fortunately, our people and the crew are well. Otherwise, this doctor would have any sick sent to the pest house on Sullivan's Island. Evans told me all this in St. John's before we left. It is well that the authorities take these protective measures."

Once the *Pretty Betsey* was cleared by the doctor and had taken a local pilot on board, she proceeded into Charles Town harbor.

"Watch on the port side. A Portuguese brigantine's going to pass us. She's homeward bound with rice. Brought Madeira wine out, no doubt," Captain Evans called to his passengers.

When the ship had passed, Major Lucas laid his hand gently on Eliza's shoulder. "Now, look toward shore, my dear. To your left is the great Ashley River. To reach our home, we will go up that river and a short way over on Wappoo Creek. We shall live on the smallest of our plantations because it is so near Charles Town. It has only six hundred acres. The one in the north on the Waccamaw and the one to the south on the Combahee River are both much larger but in less settled territory. Now, Eliza, to your right, the big river you see pouring into the harbor is the Cooper."

Eliza's beautiful eyes lit up with enthusiasm. " 'Tis a fine harbor, Papa, and so many vessels! I had not fancied there would be so many. But, indeed, I can scarcely wait to go up the Ashley to our home."

As they neared shore, the major took Cully to assist Mrs. Lucas up to the deck. As she did so often, Eliza observed and admired her father's tender care of her mother. Mrs. Lucas gasped when she saw the harbor and town. "Why, Charles Town is quite a fair sight, after all. It does not appear crude as I had feared."

There was a bustle among the sailors and a shouting of orders as the anchor was dropped. Captain Evans lowered a small boat to carry them ashore.

When Eliza first put her foot on solid ground, she thought the earth was swaying under her. Her father laughed. "You have been in motion so long, you have brought it to shore. 'Twill soon pass."

The dock was alive with people. Some were typical of any waterfront, but there were also a number of well-dressed men and a cluster of Negro nurses with small boys eager to see the ships. A middle-aged man, in a well-cut brown coat and snuff-colored waistcoat, came forward at once to greet the Lucases. His manner was one of kindly courtesy as he doffed his three-cornered hat and said, "Welcome to South Carolina, Major Lucas. I just had word your ship had cleared inspection. Samuel Millington, sir, your factor, at your service." He turned toward Mrs. Lucas and said, "Your servant, madam. I have done a man's feeble best to have your house at Wappoo in shape. The furniture that arrived earlier is in place, but I confess the residence has long been unoccupied and lacks a woman's touch." He smiled pleasantly.

Major Lucas shook hands warmly with his agent. "Splendid to see you, sir. It was your excellent reports that encouraged me to make this venture. May I present my two daughters, Polly and Mistress Eliza, who is my right hand. My sons are in school in London."

Mr. Millington turned again to Mrs. Lucas. "My wife

presents her compliments, madam, and begs you to consider our home yours until you move to Wappoo and take up plantation life."

The major promptly answered for his wife. "Sir, you and Mrs. Millington are most gracious, and we are pleased to accept your hospitality. Mrs. Lucas must rest after this rather tedious voyage. If it meets with your convenience, I would fancy a view of the town this afternoon. Then we will proceed tomorrow morning to the plantation."

Mr. Millington could not hide his surprise. "So soon? Why not tarry in town longer and taste our civilities before you repair to the country?"

"I heartily thank you, sir, but my wife longs for an end to her traveling. The sooner we settle, the better. I would like it if my daughter Eliza could accompany us on the drive around Charles Town today."

Two

Throughout the drive that afternoon, Mr. Millington told the Lucases about Charles Town and how it had grown since its founding in 1670. He reported with pride that the city had long had a library, a free school, and a newspaper. The paper, the *South Carolina Gazette,* had been started by Thomas Whitemarsh, a printer Benjamin Franklin had sent down from Philadelphia. On the death of Whitemarsh, Franklin had sent Louis Timothée to continue the newspaper.

As the carriage passed the newspaper office and printing shop, Mr. Millington said, "Like many of the French Huguenots who have settled in Charles Town, Timothée took the English form of his name, Lewis Timothy. He died recently, but his widow now sees to it that the *South Carolina Gazette* furnishes us with world news as well as reports of local doings. Mistress Eliza, being a young lady, you will like the advertisements that report whenever a ship comes in with a supply of goods for the ladies. An Englishman once told me our ladies are more fashionably dressed than those in the provinces at home."

Mr. Millington offered snuff to Major Lucas, took a pinch himself, and continued. "That building over there is our theater. *The Recruiting Officer* was the most popular play the theater produced during its first two seasons. We are hopeful that a company of players will return to give us dramatic presentations this winter. 'Tis gay indeed when there is a play, and all the gentry come in their best brocades and jewels."

"Oh, Papa, when a play is put on, may I not go?" Eliza asked eagerly. "I am old enough now. I did so long to attend the theater in London."

Polly, who had persuaded her father to let her come along and who could never stay wholly silent, now burst out, "Everyone must be very rich here, Papa. There are so many carriages. And look at that pretty box they're carrying a lady in."

Eliza laughed. "That's called a chair, Polly. I've seen them in London."

Mr. Millington smiled down at the small girl. "Polly, you are very observant. There is much wealth here already, and there will be more." Turning to Major Lucas, he continued, "Both planters and merchants have made money. The planters grow rice, raise cattle and hogs, and have their trees tapped for turpentine and felled for lumber. Then there's the manufacture of naval stores—tar and pitch. As you know, we ship much to the West Indies. Our chief export to Europe is rice. But the Crown still urges us on to find some other less bulky staple to export in addition to rice."

Major Lucas raised his eyebrows. "That interests me profoundly, Mr. Millington. I should like to hear more of that sometime. I have already given much thought to the need to try out new crops on our plantations."

Eliza listened attentively, for her father had confided in her that this move from Antigua was greatly straining his finances and that they must do all possible to make big profits from their plantation crops.

"Take us now to St. Philip's Church," Mr. Millington instructed his driver. Turning back to his guests, he said, "You must not think we are just lovers of pleasure and comfort. Our churches are well attended, and we have benevolent societies that provide for the ill and indigent."

"Splendid," Major Lucas replied.

When they reached stately St. Philip's Church, Eliza stopped a moment to kneel down to thank God for their safe voyage. She also prayed for improvement of her mother's health and for her two brothers so far away in England. When Polly tugged at her hoop skirt, however, she rose swiftly and rejoined her father and his agent.

They then visited the nearby Powder Magazine, and Mr. Millington explained to Major Lucas how the militia troops were kept ready for the defense of the province.

After they were again seated in the carriage, Mr. Millington consulted a thick gold watch. He announced, " 'Twould be no use to visit the market now. The bells ring to open it at the rising of the sun, and by this hour the vendors will have left. But I do wish I could show you how well supplied with foodstuffs we are. The fish, shrimp, oysters, and salt-marsh terrapin are especially fine here. Another favorite is the box-tortoise that many Carolinians call 'cooter.' At your plantation you will have all those and plentiful game."

As the carriage horses clopped along, Mr. Millington pointed out the houses of prominent citizens, adding, "You will see that most of our structures are of wood. The Fire Masters of town must be very diligent, and all householders have to supply buckets and ladders for use in case of fire. But one pernicious custom is permitted here that, in my opinion, Major Lucas, is a constant fire hazard. For some reason, the town fathers permit the burning of vast quantities of pine wood on the docks to draw out the tar. Of course, this does manufacture the tar close by the ships that will transport it to other colonies and abroad, but some day I look for sparks to be blown onto the wooden buildings and start a great fire."

As they drove down Church Street, Eliza noticed a pretty woman, wrapped in a handsome broadcloth mantua and holding a tiny fur muff. "The town reminds me of a small London," she remarked. "There seem many genteel people in residence."

"Yes, you will come to know them. We have charming musicals and balls in Charles Town. And the gentlemen have clubs that meet regularly at our better taverns. In the summer the plantation owners usually come to town to enjoy the sea breeze and avoid the country or bilious fever. You will be coming for the gay events then. And certainly if you are staying at your plantation on Wappoo Creek, you could come in at other times as well. Wappoo is scarce an hour from town by pettiauger."

"Pettiauger?" Eliza repeated the curious word inquiringly.

"Yes, the pettiauger is the long canoe we use on the rivers," her host explained.

"Those hollowed-out long boats we saw near the dock?" Eliza asked.

"Precisely. Early colonists borrowed the idea from the Indians and the name from the Spanish word 'piragua.' In some colonies they call them pirogues or periaguas. Our Carolina pettiaugers are made from great cypress trees. Some boats are as much as thirty feet long and will transport fifty barrels of rice. Each plantation has a boatman who is called a patroon. He directs the pettiauger crews and keeps the boats in repair."

The irrepressible Polly giggled. "Such a silly name—petti—" She broke off in a gale of merriment.

Major Lucas frowned at Polly and asked hastily, "Mr. Millington, would you say this pleasant weather is typical for this time of year? If I mistake not, today is November 15."

"Quite right, Major, and the weather is usual. We generally have a pleasant coolness in the air by now."

Major Lucas cleared his throat. "I have not yet noticed a bookseller's shop—is there one in Charles Town? I am most anxious to lay hands on Mark Catesby's *The Natural History of Carolina, Florida and the Bahama Islands.* The bookseller in Antigua was unable to get it out from London before I left. Next to my family and army career, Mr. Millington, the study of plants is my greatest interest. My daughter Eliza has developed some proficiency in that study. She might in time prove quite an amateur botanist."

Eliza blushed hard. Her father had never before praised her to a stranger.

Their visit to the bookseller was successful, and once Major Lucas's purchase was completed, Mr. Millington suggested, "Let us now return home for a dish of tea with Mrs. Lucas and my good wife. Another day, Major Lucas, I would like to show you our bastions and line of military defense."

"By all means. But you have already given us a good glance over the town. Tonight I should like to go over the accounts for my properties if you are agreeable. I shall wish you to sell the cargo of sugar I brought. And we must immediately assemble the cargo for Captain Evans to take back to Antigua. Doubtless, my overseers, Murray and Starrat, can send rice, lumber, and beef cattle promptly from the two larger plantations."

The bells of Charles Town waked Eliza Lucas early the next morning. She tiptoed to the window and drank in gulps of the brisk air, so different from that of tropical Antigua. She leaned out to look at the Millingtons' neat garden. There were several handsome magnolia trees, their leaves so glossy that they appeared to be waxed. Of course, this was not the time of the year for the great white blossoms she was so eager to smell. Mrs. Millington had told her of them the night before.

She heard a thump behind her and knew that Noni had arrived with hot water for her bath. Eliza shivered a little as she crawled into the shallow tin tub, but the hot water felt good and Noni kept pouring it from the shiny copper pot.

Eliza looked with distaste at the dignified bottle-green traveling dress she had arrived in. She hated to put it back on, but she forced herself to do so. Well, soon she could slip into gayer clothes on the plantation, she decided.

Bella, tall and stately, came into the room at that moment. "Your momma's been awake since sunup." She went on to explain that Mrs. Lucas wished the girls to bring their cloaks as it was chilly outside.

Eliza took the gay scarlet mantua Noni handed her. She had not worn it since her return from London. In the tropics there was no need for such a cloak.

Bella muttered, "Polly—in bed too long."

"No, Bella, I wanted to dress before she got up. The child is tired after yesterday. So much excitement and new sights. Noni'll wake her soon."

Eliza looked at the two maids in their gay calico blouses and full skirts of a coarse linen called Osnaburg. Each one wore a scarf becomingly tied around her head like a turban. "Be sure to put on your new wool shawls today," Eliza told them, "or you'll feel the chill. Papa has ordered warm clothing for all our people. It will be distributed after we reach the plantation."

Noni rolled her eyes and chanted happily, "New, new! New clothes for Noni." Her youthful gaiety contrasted strongly with Bella's solemn and silent ways.

At breakfast Mr. Millington explained how they would proceed. "I have arranged for the *Pretty Betsey* to carry you up the Ashley to where Wappoo Creek flows into the river. The patroon from your plantation will meet you there with the pettiaugers, as the large sloop cannot go up the creek to your own landing."

Eliza found everything exciting. The early morning bustle of Charles Town was stimulating—so different from the lazy pace of the tropics.

When they reached the dock near which the *Pretty Betsey* rode at anchor, there was a cluster of Indians sorting out a pile of furs.

"Mama," Polly screamed, "red men. They'll get us. Oh, Papa, I'm scared."

"Hush, Polly," Major Lucas declared in a stern tone. "We are at peace with the Indians. They are here to trade and will harm no one."

Eliza looked closely at the lean, almost naked American natives. The November weather seemed cool to her but evidently not to these red men, who wore little more than a breechclout, though one did, amusingly enough, have a beaver hat on his head. She had heard much talk in London about American Indians, though she had missed the visit of seven Cherokee Indian chiefs brought from South Carolina in 1730. Two of her schoolmates, however, had seen them and told her how they were presented to the King of England.

Now she whispered to her father, "They are fierce of face but very strong-looking. They must be ever so hardy not to need clothes. I would be shivering."

Major Lucas glanced over at the cluster of Indians before replying. "Yes, they keep in fine condition and are great fighters. I am glad we have a peace treaty here in South Carolina with the Cherokees, for they would be dangerous enemies."

Later, as they sailed up the Ashley River, Eliza saw more Indians paddling toward Charles Town with skins heaped in their canoes. She tried to record in her mind exactly how the Indians looked so she could write about them to Nellie Brambly and to Mrs. Boddicott, with whom she had lived while attending school in London. The thought of Mrs. Boddicott made Eliza recall the neat, placid English rivers she had seen and contrast them to this wide, tawny tributary of the sea up which they were traveling. She tingled a little at the strangeness of coming to this huge new land where no English people had made their homes until sixty-eight years before.

Just then, Captain Evans shouted, "Over on the port side up ahead, young ladies, see that creek? That's Wappoo."

Eliza strained to see the mouth of the creek and then turned her attention to the marshes that bordered the Ashley. The tall, tough grasses were bent by the breeze and moved like the green waves of the sea. Her father pointed to a V-shaped flight of black objects far in the distance. Mr. Millington, who had accompanied them, said promptly, "Ducks, Major. You'll have excellent shooting over the marshes. There's not much finer eating than a wild duck."

And now they were at the mouth of Wappoo Creek, where its tawny waters flowed into those of the Ashley. Three of the long pettiaugers, manned by tall, broad-shouldered Negroes, waited at the appointed spot.

Captain Evans dropped anchor, and the boatmen immediately rowed their pettiaugers to the side of the sloop. Eliza knew that these were some of the slaves who worked on her father's South Carolina property.

Mrs. Lucas was gently lowered into the hollowed-out log

canoe. Her faithful Bella followed close behind her. The major greeted the boatmen, and they smiled back and mumbled a welcome.

Taking Polly's hand, Eliza headed for the stern to tell Captain Evans good-by, but before Eliza could do so, he stopped them. "No farewells now, little ladies. I shall be at your home before I sail for Antigua. Your father'll be giving me instructions and a packet of letters to take back."

"Oh, then, Captain, I shall write some, too, and perhaps I can send gifts back to my friends, Miss Brambly and Miss Dunbar."

Captain Evans teased, "And maybe a letter to that handsome young ensign I saw pining over you on the wharf before we sailed?"

Eliza laughed. "Oh, he's just a friend. You forget, Captain, I am not yet sixteen."

The girls were the last to descend to the pettiaugers. As soon as Polly and Eliza were settled, Jethro, the patroon, shouted an order, and the men dipped their oars as one into the water. They quickly fell into a strong, even stroke and began a low chant to help them keep the rhythm. Eliza pinched herself to make sure it was really she in this strange craft, moving rapidly over these brown waters.

Up ahead she saw two white herons standing knee-deep in the creek. The noise of the approaching boats disturbed them at their morning fishing. They continued just as long as they safely could and then soared up on their great wings. Once in the air, they sailed lazily over a marshy inlet.

Mr. Millington, who was in the pettiauger with the girls, said to Eliza, "I see you observing the marsh, Mistress Eliza. Some of that is tare grass and some water oats. When cut green, they make good fodder for horned cattle."

Eliza looked at her father's factor in surprise. She had

22

thought of him strictly as a city merchant. "Oh," she said eagerly, "there's so much I want to learn right away. This country is so very different from either England or Antigua. Whose lands are we passing, sir?"

Mr. Millington squinted his eyes as he looked around to take his bearings before replying. "On your right, which is your father's side of the creek, we have now passed the Fenwicke and Coburg plantations. Do you see that marshy inlet ahead? After that we will pass by Mrs. Woodward's estate. She will be your next-door neighbor. A splendid woman! She is the widow of Richard Woodward, a descendant of the first South Carolinian."

Puzzled, Eliza asked, "The first—how do you mean that, Mr. Millington?"

"Well, Mistress Eliza, since we have the time, I'll tell you the story. There was a young doctor named Henry Woodward who lived in Barbados, an island lying to the south of Antigua. When King Charles II presented the province of Carolina to eight of his noble friends and named them The Lords Proprietors, those men had exploring parties from Barbados come up here to look over this Carolina grant. Young Dr. Woodward was in one of those groups. The Cassique of Kiawah, an Indian chief, greeted the white men in friendliness and helped them explore the coast."

Mr. Millington took a pinch of snuff and continued. "Woodward was much taken with the richness of the new land and asked to stay longer with the Kiawah tribe to study the area and learn to speak Indian. They treated the young doctor royally, but the Spanish soon heard of his presence and wanted no enemy English becoming a friend of the Indians. They sailed up from St. Augustine, captured Dr. Woodward, and carried him off prisoner."

"Do please tell us what happened then," Eliza urged.

"Somehow Woodward escaped to the island of Nevis, and there he was joined by settlers sent out by The Lords Proprietors to Carolina. Woodward returned to Port Royal and was warmly greeted by his Indian friends. To be farther from the Spaniards and the unfriendly Westo Indians, he and the other English came north and settled near here on the Ashley River. It was through Woodward's constant visits to the Indians to obtain food and to arrange peace treaties that the colonists were able to survive. He also was the first man to try out rice here in the colony. He had received a small bag of 'gold seed rice' from a New England sea captain who had brought it from faraway Madagascar."

"Really?" Eliza's voice showed her interest. "I believe rice is the chief crop grown as yet on Papa's Carolina lands. I want to learn all about it."

Mr. Millington smiled at the girl's unusual interest in her father's business. "Yes, yes, young lady, but not now." He pointed. "Look there among those trees. You can just see the Woodward house. Mrs. Woodward has a young daughter to whom the plantation was really left. Mrs. Woodward is her guardian and trustee. Her daughter, Mrs. Chardon, is not much older than you, but she's already a widow. She is a very beautiful young woman."

Polly had been unusually quiet, but she burst in now. "But Eliza's not yet sixteen!"

The merchant replied, "Yes, little Polly, some girls marry very young here in Carolina, and her husband, Mr. Chardon, was older than she."

Eliza was anxious to smooth over the child's outburst and said, "Oh, I shall look forward to having a young friend so near. I was fearful that there would be none."

"Now," said Mr. Millington, "after we pass this deep bend

in the creek, you will see The Bluff, as some people call your father's plantation. Most people refer to it as Wappoo."

Polly started to stand up, but her sister pulled her down to keep her from rocking the pettiauger. Eliza was tense with anticipation. This was almost like exploring a new world.

"That strip of marsh there," Mr. Millington declared, "projects up into your father's land. 'Tis an excellent spot for duck shooting, and I fancy your papa is a capital shot."

"Better than any other officer in his regiment," Polly proudly boasted.

"What are those strange things like gray veils I see hanging down from the trees?" asked Eliza.

" 'Tis called Spanish moss. You will find it very abundant here."

"It gives an odd effect, but I rather like it," she mused aloud.

"Now, young ladies, if you look hard, you can see a grove of live oak trees up on that bluff. Your home is there."

Eliza tingled at the words. A home set among live oaks—how different from Antigua or even England, where there were oaks but not this kind.

At last they arrived. Once helped onto shore, holding her skirt as high as propriety permitted, Eliza almost flew up the bank, she was so anxious to see the view from the top and to glimpse their house.

The bank was actually not more than twelve feet in height, but in this low country it seemed high. From the top she gazed out across the marsh to a sandy island and on beyond to where the sun glittered on a larger stream of water. That would be the Stono River Mr. Millington had spoken of. She ran toward the house. It was not a mansion, but it was dignified and large enough, built of wood. Eliza liked the way the gnarled live oaks formed a frame for the dwelling.

Eliza rushed back down the bank and called to her mother, who was being lifted out of the pettiauger, "Oh, Mama, you will love it. The prospect is charming."

Three

When they entered the house, Mrs. Lucas, although wearied from the morning's exertions, managed to look through some rooms of her new home. She was very pleased by what she saw. "Mr. Millington, you have very nicely placed the furniture we shipped earlier. As soon as the lighter pieces arrive from the sloop, the place will look very livable."

The agent bowed gracefully at the compliment. "You are very kind indeed, madam," he said. "I took the liberty of having fires made in all the rooms, as the house has been so long closed. In addition to this parlor, there is the dining room and small library on this floor and the master chamber. Mrs. Millington sent linens over yesterday so that the bed there might be made."

Mrs. Lucas was much affected by this further kindness.

Major Lucas said tenderly to his wife, "My dear, I think Bella had best attend you so that you may retire for some rest. Eliza, take Polly upstairs to the other bedrooms and choose which each of you wishes to occupy."

Then the newly arrived owner went out for an inspection of the stable and barn and the quarters where his servants would live with the other Negro slaves. He wished to go over the buildings with his factor before Mr. Millington had to return to Charles Town.

The pettiaugers and the plantation's flat batteau had been sent back to the *Pretty Betsey,* and they now brought the Lucases' delicate furniture and personal possessions from the sloop. Eliza took charge of placing them. She was assisted by Cully, who had already secured two of the field hands from the slave quarters to work with him. "Cully, see that the men set the harpsichord down gently. I do hope it was not damaged on board ship. Place it here by the window where I can see the water as I play. Papa's kettledrums should go here. No, please don't put that box there. Those are books. Follow me to the library."

Eliza moved off swiftly. Although small of stature, she radiated a quiet authority, which she had acquired during her mother's illness.

There was much to do but many hands to do it, and soon there was a semblance of order.

Polly came running in from the yard, followed by her nurse. "Sister, sister," the child babbled, "there's an old man and a boy coming up the path with a great big basket."

Eliza went to the door and was on hand to greet the two who were indeed carrying a huge hamper. The old man bowed. He was too winded to speak but handed Eliza a note. He motioned to his helper, and they brought the hamper in and set it on the floor. Then the grizzled old man proudly lifted a white damask cloth to reveal a baked ham, two cooked ducks, crisp rolls, fresh butter, a wedge of cheddar cheese, and blackberry tarts.

Eliza swiftly opened the note to see who had provided so generously for them. She read:

A welcome to our shores from your near neighbors. With your permission, my daughter, Mrs. Chardon, and I will call as soon as you are settled.

Sarah Woodward

Polly scampered up to peer in the basket and snatched a tart before Eliza could tell Cully to take the food to the kitchen.

"It was most kind of your mistress to think of us in this way," Eliza said smilingly to her neighbor's servant. "If you will wait a few moments, Cully is emptying the basket for you to take back now. Please thank Mrs. Woodward for my mother and for us all. I will send a note over later."

"Yas'm, glad to tell her." The old man was smiling as he hobbled off.

"Noni, run out to the cookhouse and see if they've washed the Canton-ware Hallie has been unpacking. And then come set the table. Now we can offer a meal suitable for Mr. Millington." Eliza's face was alight with pleasure over this happy development.

When Major Lucas and Mr. Millington returned from their tour of inspection, all was in readiness. The major found only one fault. He turned to Cully, who was bringing in a platter of food, and asked, "What wine are you serving?"

The white-haired Cully, who took great pride in his work, looked mortified and glanced in distress at Eliza.

She quickly intervened. "Papa, Cully told me that the wine is 'shook up' from the trip here, and we didn't think you'd want it."

"It will be cloudy," Major Lucas agreed, "but we must have a toast at our first meal in our new home."

Cully brought a bottle of Madeira, and the major proposed a toast, first to the King and then another to Mr. Millington, who had showed them such kindness.

Mr. Millington promptly returned the compliment by proposing, "The Lucases! May Providence provide health, happiness, and prosperity."

"I thank you kindly, sir. I do trust my wife will strengthen. She sends her apologies that she could not join us."

Mrs. Woodward had included in the hamper several sea bass, already cleaned. These had been at the bottom of the basket, and Eliza had not seen them because they had been carefully wrapped. The fish had been cooked by Cully's wife, Hallie, and were served along with the cold viands from the basket.

Major Lucas was particularly pleased and, after praising the fish, announced, "I think I shall assign one of my men to fish three days a week. That should keep our table in fresh supply and the quarters as well."

And then, to make amends for Cully's discomfiture about the wine, the major turned to his butler standing behind him. "Tell Hallie she has grilled this fish to perfection. I send my compliments, for I know it is not easy to start cooking in a new kitchen."

Late that afternoon an elderly gentleman rode up the sandy lane on the land side of the Lucas house. Eliza and her father were outside, already discussing where they would place flower borders. Major Lucas walked toward the horseman as he dismounted.

The visitor made a sweeping old-fashioned bow and said, "Sir, may I present myself as your neighbor, Andrew Deveaux of Westpenny plantation. Our properties do not join, unfortunately, but we are near. Though Tiger Swamp and Hillsborough lie between us, I trust we shall see each other often."

Eliza was introduced and immediately liked the bright-eyed gentleman who spoke with a decided French accent.

Major Lucas turned to his guest. "We are indeed fortunate

to have such neighbors as you and Mrs. Woodward. 'Pon my word, you have shown us great civility. Shall we go in? I was about to have a hot rum punch, Mr. Deveaux, as I feel the evening chill after my long residence in the tropics. Pray be so kind as to join me."

The three entered the house, and Eliza slipped away to have the punch made. As she left, her father called to her, "Daughter, do come back and have a dish of tea with us. We must both learn all we can of planting from Mr. Deveaux. I can see he will be a fine source of information and a guide to us."

When Eliza returned with the punch, the two men broke off their conversation about rice culture. "Sir, this is most pleasant," remarked Mr. Deveaux. "How I envy you a daughter, sir! I have only sons."

Major Lucas replied, "My two boys are in England, so Eliza is my aide-de-camp. Tell me, Mr. Deveaux, have you long resided here?"

"I came to live in this section upon my wife's inheritance of Westpenny plantation. You may have noticed my French name. I am a Huguenot, sir, and married a widow, Madame Girardeau. Indeed, our lands are an inheritance from her father, Monsieur Le Sade."

Major Lucas replied, "I am pleased at this opportunity to express my admiration for the Huguenots. You have suffered much for your convictions, but you have never faltered. I also admire your industry. I have heard that you seek to create a real silk culture here."

Mr. Deveaux waved thin, expressive hands. "That has long been a hope, but raising silk cocoons has now been largely abandoned in South Carolina. I do not go in for it at Westpenny."

Eliza smiled at the visitor and remarked, "The name of your seat, Westpenny, is so unusual. Am I wrong in thinking it not French?"

"No, my child, my wife's people say it came from the Indians, who called it Westpanee."

" 'Twas an experience to actually see Indians on our way here. But, tell me, Mr. Deveaux, please, are we far from the church of this parish?"

"No, 'tis no great distance to St. Andrew's. The road is not a broad highway but 'tis passable, or you could go by boat. Many Carolinians prefer a smooth trip by pettiauger to a bumpy one by carriage. It has been said the rivers are our highways."

"I expect Eliza and I will ride, Mr. Deveaux. We have horses, but I brought no carriage," declared Major Lucas.

"Indeed, why not ride? Many of our neighbors go on horseback, especially the men. I myself usually go by pettiauger into Charles Town for the Huguenot service at the French church."

Major Lucas leaned forward eagerly. "Mr. Deveaux, pray tell me how you schedule your winter work at Westpenny and how early in the spring you start rice planting?"

And so the conversation again turned to the talk of crops and plantation affairs.

Without any discussion of the matter, it was understood that, because of her mother's illness, Eliza would take over the duties usually handled by the mistress of a plantation. She had received a superior schooling in London during her years there, where she had lived with kindly Mr. and Mrs. Boddicott. But Eliza was wiser than her fifteen and a half years, chiefly because of the interest her father had taken in developing her abilities.

Major Lucas confided in Eliza that he would have to devote all his efforts to get the fields and stables in first-class condition. He promised her the assistance of whichever servants she required to get the house and slave quarters in order and gave her a free hand in the task, adding affectionately, "You know what our people need, and I can count on you to practice every economy that does not deprive them."

Eliza's first concern was to distribute the warm clothing that had been brought from Mr. Millington's warehouse in Charles Town. Upset over the uncomfortable and dirty condition of the slave quarters, she set herself to put them in good shape.

Major Lucas had sent orders ahead to have Pompey the carpenter, Sogo the cooper, and Dick the smith brought to Wappoo from his fifteen-hundred-acre Garden Hill plantation, located some forty miles to the southwest on the Combahee River. After going over his daughter's proposed improvements with her, Major Lucas told Pompey, "You do exactly what Mistress Eliza wishes done."

And so, as soon as the row of cabins had been given a drastic cleaning, Eliza ordered Pompey and Sogo to take men and knock out any chinking between the logs that was loose and then to repack and daub them tight with fresh mud. She placed Cully in charge of supervising the whitewashing of every wall, inside and out. Otelia, a motherly-looking Negress who was respected for her understanding of sickness, supervised the scrubbing of floors.

Eliza tried to assign the freshly renovated cabins as fairly as she could among the twenty adult Negroes and thirty some children who were to live and work at Wappoo.

When she had finished, she sent again for Pompey the carpenter. "We must have a nursery for the small children before the mothers can leave them to do any work," she told him. "Fetch Dick the smith, and you can have Cully and any of the men you need till that is built. None of these cabins is big enough to use for the children."

Major Lucas agreed with Eliza that this was the first construction job needed, and eight men were set to cutting and skinning tall pines in the nearby woods. Pompey was told to train Ezra, just arrived in the *Pretty Betsey* with the Lucases. Ezra must be taught the method of building a log house. The construction of the nursery or "child house," as Eliza learned to call it, was a jolly affair. All the small Negro children kept vigilant watch to recover chips from the ax wielders and built their own play huts. Eliza watched them at play and soon allowed Polly to join the fun. When the children tired of that, they sang and did their shuffling little dances.

A merry-faced boy fastened sticks on his fingers and clacked them together to make a noisy rhythm. To this he did a jig of his own invention. Noni was horrified when she found the boy teaching young Polly to do his dance, but Eliza said to let her sister learn.

There were some shingles on hand but not quite enough for the roof. Sogo, Dick, and Ezra worked laboriously at splitting some shingles out of cypress wood. Finally they were finished, and the new house was roofed in.

As the last shingles were being nailed in place, Otelia came up to Eliza and expressed her pleasure over the "child house," but she asked where they were going to take care of any who fell sick now that there were so many more slaves living in the quarters.

There were two empty cabins down at the far end of the row that were not needed for families. Being at the end, no one had wanted them particularly. Sogo had said their roofs needed repairing but could be fixed. Eliza decided she could use one for men and one for women who were ailing and join the two cabins by a covered porch or runway.

That evening Eliza waited until after supper to tackle her father on her idea. "Papa, I know you are anxious to start Pompey, Dick, and Sogo on repairing the barn, but may I not keep them long enough to fix up an infirmary? We must be ready if any of our people should fall ill. Otelia has much skill in caring for her people. She asked for a 'sick house' where she can keep them in bed away from their families and told me that Mr. Deveaux has one on his plantation. Dick killed two snakes today and says our people from Antigua have got to look out for them, and Sogo says fever or dysentery might come on the newcomers."

Major Lucas ran his hand wearily over his face. "I cannot wait much longer, daughter. However, our people must be cared for, so you may proceed as you have suggested. After that I *must* have any man that can handle tools."

Eliza was delighted when the infirmary was finished and she had started an old woman called Sairy in her routine of caring for the small children in the child house. Now, she could turn her attention to putting their own home in order. She placed her father's books on the shelves in the small library, which he would also use as an office; she hung pictures, fixed the linen neatly in a cupboard with lavender bags, and set up one cupboard with medicines in case of sickness.

Eager as she was to do all she could to help her father, Eliza was now hungry for some gaiety. She loved parties, and as their neighbors had promised a round of them, she longed for it to begin. She could hardly wait to meet the young people of their neighborhood.

Four

Mrs. Lucas was forced to stay in bed. She was having a reaction from the excitement of the long trip and the change of climate, though she had made an effort and dressed to receive their next-door neighbors, Mrs. Woodward and her pretty young daughter, Mrs. Chardon, when they called shortly after the Lucases had arrived at Wappoo. Now that Eliza felt things were in sufficient order for her to go calling, her mother urged her to repay their next-door neighbors' visit. Major Lucas decided he should accompany the two girls since his wife did not feel up to the exertion.

After the usual greetings, Major Lucas happened to look out of the window and spied a pony grazing in a field near the house. He remarked on the animal's fine head.

"Well, the pony's not young, but he is very gentle," Mrs. Woodward said. "It is a shame there is no child here to ride him."

"Forgive me if I presume too much, but might you possibly consider selling the pony to me for my daughter Polly? I wish her to learn to ride so she can go out with Eliza and me around the plantation. Eliza can teach her. She has more patience than I, even though she resembles me in her liking for prompt action."

Mrs. Woodward looked surprised but turned to her

daughter. "My dear, would you have any objection to selling the pony? Ronnie is growing fat from lack of exercise."

Young Mrs. Chardon called Polly over to her. "Would you promise to be kind to Ronnie?"

"Oh, indeed yes! I am not mean like a boy who lived near us in Antigua. He twisted his cat's tail. I like animals, and they like me." Polly gave an impish grin.

Mrs. Chardon and Mrs. Woodward both laughed, and before many minutes the purchase of the pony had been arranged. The sidesaddle Mrs. Chardon had used as a girl was thrown in on the sale.

Mrs. Woodward said, "As we mentioned at your house, we want so much to give an oyster roast to introduce your other neighbors to you."

Before her mother could continue, Mrs. Chardon declared enthusiastically, "We do hope you have come to tell us when we may have the event."

"You are most gracious, dear ladies, but for the next few days I shall be busy assembling cargo to go back to Antigua in the *Pretty Betsey,*" replied Major Lucas. And I know Eliza will be writing letters to go by Captain Evans. Perhaps my wife will be stronger by then."

"Oh, Major, pray do let us set a date for a week from now. It will take us that long to send notes out to the neighbors and to make preparations," persisted the hospitable Mrs. Woodward.

Eliza looked pleadingly at her father, and Polly scampered over to his side and snuggled against him. Putting her lips close to his ear, she said in a loud whisper, "Dear Papa, say yes. A party'd make Mama feel better."

Major Lucas laughed heartily and declared, "Ladies, my family and I will be delighted to accept for a week from today."

Eliza could scarcely stop talking about the oyster roast on the ride home. Like any other fifteen-year-old girl, she was pleased she could wear the new flowered gown that had been made for her just before they had left Antigua.

"Oh, I hope Mama will be able to go," Polly cried.

Her father replied in a patient but not altogether hopeful way, "I shall certainly urge and encourage her to do so."

When the day finally came, Mrs. Lucas surprised and delighted her family by going to the party.

The oyster roast proved a delightful affair and not so formal as entertainments back in St. John's had been.

At the party were gathered the Rose family from nearby Accabee plantation, Linings from Hillsborough plantation, Savages, Fenwickes, Godfreys, Bulls from Ashley Hall, the Draytons of Drayton Hall and others. The Reverend William Guy, rector of St. Andrew's Church, was among those present, as were Mr. and Mrs. Deveaux.

Assembling at two o'clock, the guests watched the skilled Negroes roast the oysters over a great outdoor fire. The aroma whetted appetites, as did the December weather. A bright sun kept the day from being too cool.

Serving maids passed through the crowd with salvers laden with food. The roasted oysters were the favorites of the day, but there were also small roasted marsh birds, sliced ham, jugged hare, and baskets of crisp hot rolls. There were homemade pickles and vegetables for those who wanted them. And there was hot chocolate and tea, as well as toddies for the men.

After many introductions, Eliza heard Mrs. Woodward say, "Major Lucas, Henry Middleton sent his deep regrets that he could not be here to meet you. He has such a vast interest in plants that I know you two will find much to discuss. He has brought over two English landscape gardeners to turn Middleton Place into a show garden. They are creating broad formal terraces, and 'tis said the changes will take several years."

"Mr. Deveaux told me of Mr. Middleton. I shall be honored to make the acquaintance of such a man, whenever it is possible."

Eliza, who had a flair for fashionable dress, was discreetly observing the stylish costumes of the ladies present. The guests reminded her of a similar group she had seen at a lawn party near London when she was visiting one of her schoolmates. These gentlemen, too, all wore well-polished buckled shoes and expertly cut suits.

But Eliza's chance to observe was cut short as various of the neighbors engaged her in conversation and especially one young man, who hovered around constantly. A visitor at Drayton Hall, Robert Leicester was presented by Mr. Drayton. Leicester, who was called Rob, saw to it that Eliza had as many of the succulent oysters as she could eat. He himself did full justice to the platters of meats as well, declaring affably, "You behold, Mistress Eliza, one of the province's finest trenchermen at work. Today, I am fair famished."

Eliza gave her low tinkling laugh, which had a way of making things seem very gay. She had to tilt her head to look at him, for he was tall.

"Do tell me how you liked school in England, Miss Eliza. I, too, was studying there until I was recalled to Carolina by the death of my father," Rob said.

Eliza was happy to talk of her school days, and the two chatted gaily of London for some minutes. To their delight they discovered they had a mutual friend. But Eliza soon maneuvered the conversation toward talk of plantation life.

"Oh, Mr. Leicester," she cried in a burst of eagerness, "I do feel so ignorant. Pray satisfy my curiosity on several points. Is it true that Scotch settlers have tried to grow the indigo plant here but have not been too successful?"

Rob Leicester raised his eyebrows and let out a low whistle of amazement. " 'Pon my word, Miss Eliza, surely one so dainty and feminine as you are has more interest in balls and music than such men's talk."

Eliza flushed and smoothed her high-swept hair. "Oh," she said and, leaning forward, whispered engagingly, "Of course I am as vain as the next girl you will meet, and I dote on pretty clothes and every possible frolic. Dancing simply enchants me."

Rob was obviously relieved. "Whew, for a moment there you startled me. I never had a young lady ask me about crops. And I, for one, prefer fencing lessons and militia drills to raising rice. May I say I find you as charming a damsel as ever set foot in this royal province."

Eliza curtsied gracefully at the flowery compliment, but as she rose, she murmured, "Do answer my question, just to satisfy an idle curiosity. I confess to a vast interest in plants and planting. My father is not o'er fond of embroidery and such things for me. I will share a small secret with you." She leaned forward and whispered, "He says the ladies only do them to find a chance to gossip together."

Rob was caught off guard and roared with laughter, for he had often seen ladies in Charles Town busily plying the embroidery needle while ripping the reputations of others. He took a long look at Eliza. Truly she was different, and he found her entrancing. She barely came to his shoulder in height and was slender without being at all thin. This pleased Rob, who despised bony females. Eliza's eyes, beautifully shaped, were extremely large and very expressive. When complimented, she had a habit of looking down that Rob was sure was not affected. It gave her a delightful air of modesty, but he did like the way she gazed straight at him when she spoke. There was a transparent honesty about her that was not at all like the simpering of some of the girls he knew. He decided Eliza really wanted an answer to the question that had so astonished him.

Rob launched out. "To be frank, Miss Eliza, I am not very well informed. I have heard that a few Scotch and also some of the Huguenots have tried their hand at indigo growing, but no one has successfully raised crops and then gone on to produce the blue dye that is so valuable. Earlier there was some silk culture, but indigo is still a bare hope in South Carolina. And now, pray tell me, do you like to ride?"

"Oh, very much, and I also admit to dearly loving the harpsichord and all forms of music. I much wish to hear the organ at St. Philip's."

Rob looked enormously pleased. "Would you permit me to ride over some day from Drayton Hall? I play the flute, and perhaps we could have a duet or two."

At this moment Mrs. Woodward interrupted them. "We are going to repair to the house now for a little musicale. Mr. Pelham, who teaches my daughter, will accompany her while she sings."

Mrs. Chardon sang prettily, and Eliza rejoiced once again to think they were near neighbors.

After the music, many of the other young people claimed Eliza's attention, but Rob Leicester persisted in plying her with the punch and currant cakes that were being served.

The neighbors were most gracious in expressing their welcome to Major and Mrs. Lucas, as well as Eliza. Said Mr. Drayton, "I think I speak for all planters whose homes are on or near the Ashley River when I declare our pleasure that you have taken up your seat here and will grace our little society."

The festivities ended with many friendly farewells but not before Rob Leicester had asked permission of Major Lucas to come calling.

Eliza's father rode home in a far more cheerful mood than when he had come and could not forbear teasing his daughter about the striking blue-eyed Rob Leicester, who wore his blond hair tied back but not powdered—a fashion that was beginning to be adopted by some younger men.

In the days that followed, Eliza found herself busy entertaining the many neighbors who came to call. Tea was served to the ladies and possets of hot rum or claret punch to the gentlemen. Mrs. Lucas received them whenever she could, but the effort only seemed to deepen her weariness.

Tall, lithe Rob Leicester came often. Eliza was pleased to find he had a pleasant tenor voice, and they spent much time around the harpsichord. Frequently, however, Rob arrived when Eliza was about to set out to ride around the plantation, and so he would join her. The young Carolinian found it hard to accept Eliza's interest in plantation management. He was always declaring, "Why should you learn these things? You must come soon to Charles Town for some gaiety. You are far too charming to be hid here on the banks of the Wappoo."

Among those who paid a visit was Henry Middleton, of Middleton Place, who came not only to "do his manners" but also to invite Major Lucas to a deer drive he was soon to hold on his plantation. The major was greatly pleased, for he was a fine shot.

Eliza thoroughly enjoyed all the callers, and she also liked seeing many of them again after church on Sundays at St. Andrew's. The congregation sat demurely in the dignified brick structure, shaped like a cross. The chancel was handsome, the roof of cypress wood well arched. The place lent itself to worship. Some dozed, but most of the people listened to the Reverend William Guy's long sermons. Eliza noticed that they sang the last hymn with great fervor and then streamed out as fast as possible to chat with each other and catch up on the week's news. She liked them for being so human.

Major Lucas, conversing with the rector after their second Sunday at St. Andrew's, asked, "Was the church this large from the beginning?"

"No, the transept was added in 1723, for the congregation had by then outgrown the original rectangular structure. The gallery was added, too."

Eliza was trying to work up courage to ask Mr. Guy a question. She could never find out enough about Indians, and she had heard someone mention that the rector had had a severe experience with them. "Mr. Guy," she inquired, "is it true that you were once attacked by Indians?"

The clergyman's kindly face wrinkled in a smile as he replied, " 'Pon my soul, young lady, you hear things fast. Yes, 'tis a fact—but that was long ago at Port Royal. The Yamassees attacked us and were joined by the Catawbas and Creeks. After that I was sent way up to New England to preach at a place called Narragansett. I missed the radiant skies of Carolina and sought permission to serve again here. I trust you will like it in South Carolina as much as I do."

Eliza smiled in a way she had that started at her large eyes and spread to her whole face. She said, "I already like it vastly, sir."

For some weeks Eliza had noticed that her father kept on the desk in his small library a copy of the *South Carolina Gazette,* of November 23. She remembered the day Captain Evans had come to settle accounts and get his instructions for delivering the return cargo to Antigua. The sloop master had brought that particular copy of the Charles Town paper and chatted with her father about the news in it.

Her curiosity finally getting the better of her, she asked her father, "Do you plan to purchase some of the items advertised in this paper or is it the mention of negotiations with Spain that causes you to keep this particular issue?"

Major Lucas smiled indulgently at his daughter and replied, "Those observing eyes of yours have missed nothing. Indeed, I must admit 'tis the Spanish news makes me keep it near me. But I am heartened by one report—that Mr. Keene, the British minister to the Court of Madrid, advised that 'the King of Spain had a stronger inclination to accommodate affairs with Great Britain than he was thought to have.' "

"Does that mean the peace treaty *will* be signed?"

"It is the best hope I have seen that real peace will be established between England and Spain. And you know what that means to me—'tis my assurance that I may stay on here in South Carolina away from my regiment."

The girl peered over her father's shoulder at the paper, which he had now spread before him. "Papa, look at that list." She pointed to a news item. "I had no idea there were twenty-six British men-of-war roaming the seas! And fifty-five in commission in the home waters! That's a fine fleet, isn't it? It makes me feel quite safe."

"Yes, my dear, but this additional statement disturbs me." He read aloud, 'If war should come, there would soon be thirteen or fourteen more put into commission.' That means there is still grave doubt that the treaty will be signed."

He pushed back his chair and rose. Then, talking as he strode back and forth, he said most seriously, "Eliza, my child, if the negotiations do fail and war threatens, you know my duty would be to return promptly to my regiment. Should such a dreadful development come soon, I could not risk that strenuous voyage again for your mother. Besides, if war were about to break, some fiery Spanish ship captain might jump the gun and attack. No, if those bad tidings come, I have decided I would have to leave the three of you here." His voice revealed his distress.

He went over to Eliza, who could not hide her surprise at his decision, and taking her hand, put it to his cheek and held it there tenderly. His eyes searched her face.

Eliza stretched up on tiptoe and gave him a light kiss. "Papa, dear, please don't fret over us. If you must go, we would manage. *You* have not made fun of my wanting to learn about the plantation; I am observing all I can."

"Yes, my child, but 'tis heavy work. Would you not rather be in Charles Town if I have to go? Doubtless, I could lease a house there."

"No, no, I'd much prefer to be here on our plantation, our very own land, and 'twould be so much quieter and more restful for Mama," Eliza replied calmly.

"Well, Cully is utterly reliable. I have never known a more faithful or intelligent house servant," Major Lucas said thoughtfully. "Mr. Millington vouches for Jethro. Of course, Mr. Millington, as my factor, would keep an eye on you. We know the women servants would be faithful, and our neighbors hereabouts have proved their kindness."

He sighed deeply and with an effort said, "Enough of that gloomy talk. May Providence forbid that such a course should ever become necessary."

Eliza was relieved to see her father try to shake off the thought of war. She said, "Do sit at your desk, Papa, and let me stroke your forehead the way you like." Her small hands were skillful, and as she massaged her father's temples gently, it soothed him. After a while she introduced a new subject.

" 'Tis nearing Christmas. Should we not make some preparations? Even though Mama is ill, should we not plan some gaiety for our people? And for Polly, too? She has always had such gay Christmases in Antigua!"

Major Lucas straightened up and reached to a shelf for his almanac. "Egad, I had forgotten the passage of time. Yes, we must secure gifts and make it a merry time this first Christmas in our new home. You make lists, Eliza, and we will journey to Charles Town for a shopping spree."

The prospect delighted Eliza, and perhaps the break in routine would cheer her father, too.

Major Lucas rang for Cully. "Send a runner for the patroon while I write a note to my factor in Charles Town. I wish you to take it yourself."

That night, Cully returned bearing a note from Mr. Millington asking the major and Eliza to spend at least one night in town, since it would take time to make a selection of goods.

And so a lighthearted Eliza packed her flower-sprigged silk dress in a portmanteau, dressed in her bottle green traveling costume, and with her father set off early the next morning for Charles Town.

In the pettiauger Major Lucas announced, "I wish to secure more shoes for our people from Millington, as I would prefer to have Jeemy split rails for fencing than try to do the cobbling. Also, my dear, I mean to purchase a great bell that will sound clearly for the workers. That conch-shell horn we have been using is not loud enough to be heard in the new fields we are clearing."

"Papa, please may we buy more supplies for my medical

chest? I have used up everything that is good for rheumatism on old Sairy. Otelia has rubbed her every day, and now she is able to go right after the children when they are naughty and run out of the child house."

Major Lucas chuckled since he had seen Sairy pursuing a young charge.

Not wanting her father's attention diverted from her medical needs, Eliza announced quickly, "I need aniseed, carthamus, brimstone, and syrup of colt's foot. If I could have some laudanum to ease pain, 'twould be a great help. Mrs. Woodward advised me to lay it in, for she said men sometimes injure themselves badly cutting trees and I could ease their suffering. I would give only the tiniest amount, just as she told me. Once she had to use it for one of her men who broke his arm while cutting a giant cypress in the swamp."

"We will secure what we can; all those things may not be on hand. You may shop for shawls and ribbons while I go to Mr. Millington's tailor. It does not look well to wear my army uniform while I am living the life of a planter."

Eliza smiled at her father. She was pleased that he was to have a new suit cut, for surely this must mean he felt he would be staying on.

It was a busy day, for the young housekeeper had a long list. She purchased yards of fustian and linen, a new Dutch blanket for her mother, three pounds of sewing thread, spices, Toledo almonds, currants and raisins, a chest of Hyson tea, and a barrel of white biscuits from England to use at teatime.

After securing these, she sought her father's advice. "May I buy some bright-colored chintz so I can make new curtains for Mama's room? The ones we brought with us are not pleasing there."

"Pray do so," said Major Lucas. "And do get your mother

some Flanders lace for her nightcaps. She asked for that."

Turning to the clerk who was waiting on him, Major Lucas said, "I wish blue waistcoats of fearnought wool for my patroon and three boatmen. Then I would like twelve worsted caps for men—the kind that sailors wear. My men are not accustomed to cold."

He asked Eliza if she were buying head kerchiefs for the women.

"Yes, I am, and sugar sticks for them and the children. Will you get tobacco for the men?" she asked her father.

"Most assuredly," replied Major Lucas. "I am also going to indulge in a fiddle for Cully. I heard him playing a gourd fiddle that Maui had made, and he deserves a better instrument. I think Cully will prove as good a fiddler as Mr. Deveaux's man."

After the Christmas buying, Major Lucas went to John Laurens's establishment to purchase a new saddle. When the two shoppers reached Mr. Millington's house in midafternoon, the factor's wife greeted them warmly. "I am so pleased that you have returned. You must be tired. Perhaps you might like a nap before teatime.

"We have invited the Honorable and Mrs. Charles Pinckney for tea. Charles Pinckney is one of our most distinguished citizens. Though still quite young, he is the Speaker of our Commons House of Assembly and one of the leading lawyers of the province. He has long been a colonel of the militia, too. Colonel Pinckney also takes great interest in his plantation, Belmont. It is about five miles up the Neck from town. My husband is eager for you two gentlemen to know each other, Major Lucas."

Eliza was delighted that her father was to have this new diversion. As a military man, he had been accustomed to the company of other men of ability. And she herself was eager to meet more Carolinians.

At tea, Eliza promptly lost her heart to the guests of honor. She decided they were the most charming people she had yet met in South Carolina. Charles Pinckney was hearty-looking, his face strong but yet revealing good humor and kindness. His handsome brown eyes radiated warmth and interest in others. Mrs. Pinckney was gracious and friendly. She made Eliza feel at ease by telling her that she, too, was the daughter of a British army officer and had grown up in London.

Mr. Millington cleared his throat to get attention. "Major Lucas, before Colonel Pinckney became the Speaker of our Assembly in 1736, he served as Attorney General of the province. Every man in Charles Town admires his common sense as well as his knowledge of law. Colonel Pinckney studied at the Inner Temple in London, Major."

The gentleman under discussion held up a hand in deprecation and said laughingly, "I protest, Millington. You will alarm these good people. Such flattery! You sound more like a courtier than a merchant, my esteemed friend."

Everyone laughed except Mrs. Millington, who had little sense of humor. "Oh, sir," she protested, " 'tis nothing compared to what he says about you in praise behind your back."

Mrs. Pinckney smoothed everything over by saying, "Ah, Mr. Millington, I see we share the same opinion of my husband. He is indeed exceptional," and she smiled at her husband affectionately.

Talk flowed freely among the congenial group. There was a discussion of the most recent news from London, of sugar raising in Antigua and the other islands, of rice culture, the high cost of purchasing a post chaise, and of the latest essays by Alexander Pope. Charles Pinckney stated his disapproval of Pope's satiric attack on the Royal Court in his most recent book, and Mr. Millington frankly admitted he did not care for satire.

During a lull in the conversation, Mrs. Pinckney suddenly turned to Major Lucas. "Pray, sir, let us have Miss Eliza with us for some of the gaieties when the season begins in Charles Town. Meanwhile, could she not come for a visit at Belmont? It is lovely on the Neck at this time of year."

"You are gracious indeed, madam. Did I understand you to say the Neck? Mrs. Millington also used that expression, I believe."

Mrs. Pinckney smiled. "Oh, we forget that everyone does not know we call the land that stretches between Charles Town and the mainland the Neck. Our plantation is there."

"That is surely a conveniently located plantation," remarked Major Lucas.

Charles Pinckney joined in then. "It is indeed, sir. But I want to second my wife's excellent proposal. Why do you not spare Miss Eliza to us for a visit in early January? We might arrange a little dance. By then my best fiddler should be recovered. He was thrown by a colt he was training and broke his arm. 'Tis now nearly mended, though."

"Oh, Major, pray let Miss Eliza go. She will meet so many of our local society and particularly the young people," Mrs. Millington urged.

The major yielded without demur. "I should be delighted, and I feel sure Mrs. Lucas will join her consent to mine. A thousand thanks."

Eliza was enchanted and added her thanks to her father's. What pleasure to look forward to!

Turning to Eliza, Charles Pinckney asked, "Have you read *Gulliver's Travels* or Defoe's *Robinson Crusoe?"*

Eliza's eyes sparkled with interest, "Oh, yes. I found Gulliver most entertaining. I think I prefer the Lilliputians, but perhaps you like the Brobdingnagians best?"

"You know, Miss Eliza, I have never really made up my mind on that point. I think it is Swift's vivid imagination that delights me most. A truly remarkable wit."

"Indeed, and quite different from Defoe's. Papa read *Robinson Crusoe* aloud to me and my brothers before they left for school in England." Eliza's eyes always shone when she talked of books.

Turning, Colonel Pinckney remarked to Major Lucas, "That is certainly a book that all ages can enjoy. In addition to general reading, sir, I presume you, as a military man, devote time to works on strategy and tactics and the history of war."

"I do indeed," responded George Lucas. "In my evenings now I am studying a book on methods of laying siege to a city."

Charles Pinckney looked serious and asked, "Have you any news of developments with Spain, Major Lucas?"

"No, no news, but I grow less optimistic of peace. I believe that we all have hunches or intimations at times, and I have one now that the negotiations are very nearly at a standstill."

Charles Pinckney looked at the officer with a new interest. "I myself have reached the same conclusion. I had recently a letter from a judge in London, a man who taught me law in the Inner Temple. He declared that Spain has no leanings to peace, that their negotiating has been essentially for purposes of delay."

"And doubtless your friend moves in circles that have inside knowledge?" Major Lucas queried grimly.

"He does," replied Colonel Pinckney, "and he often knows much before 'tis made public."

Five

To Eliza's great pleasure, the weather at Wappoo suddenly turned quite frosty. "I do declare," she remarked happily to her father, "I almost feel as if I were back in England. I shall never forget the crisp, busy days there before Christmas. Mrs. Boddicott made so many special dishes for the holidays, and I loved helping her. She said it was part of my English education."

" 'Tis fortunate indeed, Eliza, that you had that opportunity, for your mother is not yet strong enough to supervise the kitchen preparations here," Major Lucas replied.

"Oh, she must not even attempt it, Papa. I have gathered receipts for cakes and pies from Mrs. Woodward, and I have Mama's own for plum pudding," Eliza said proudly. "Otelia and her two girls are going to help Hallie with the preparations."

Major Lucas raised one eyebrow in mock amazement. "Well, my charming daughter, you seem to have things well in hand in the culinary department. This cold weather suits me splendidly, for it means I can proceed today with the slaughter of the hogs. The temperature is now low enough to preserve the fresh pork for a Christmas feast for our people. Mr. Deveaux tells me that is a custom here."

In the outside kitchen, Eliza began assembling the ingredients for mincemeat and reading Mrs. Woodward's receipt to Hallie. Then she set Otelia and her young daughters to chopping up nuts and fruits for the fruitcake. The cake was the first thing ready to go into the oven at the side of the huge brick fireplace. Delicious spicy aromas began to fill the room, and Polly burst into the kitchen to know how soon she could have something to eat. Hallie whispered to the child that she was to have a tiny cake of her own and that it would be ready first of all. Polly responded with a funny little gurgle of delight. "Be sure to keep it just for me, Hallie. I'll be back soon. I promised my pony a gallop," Polly called as she ran outside.

Perched on a stool, Eliza studied a receipt that Mrs. Woodward had confided was her "pride and joy." It was for a tart made of sweet potato, flavored with lemon and orange, and fluffed with white of egg. Eliza had never had these tarts before and was most anxious to make a success of them since her parents had invited Mrs. Woodward and her daughter to Christmas dinner.

For three days the kitchen resounded with the sound of wooden spoon stirring and beating, with the clump of wood as Otelia's young son dropped log after log on the roaring open fire, and with happy talk and laughter.

Sampling each mixture, Eliza pursed up her mouth as she had seen Mrs. Boddicott do while deciding whether more flavoring was needed. It was slow work, baking in the chimney oven, but one by one nicely browned cakes, pies, and tarts were drawn forth by a triumphant Hallie. Eliza was both relieved and proud because she had not been nearly so sure that she knew how to direct the preparations as she had pretended to her father.

Polly, having come in to beg for a mincemeat tart, took a sharp look at her sister, who was putting on her crimson cloak. "Eliza, your face is as red as your mantua, and your hair's not very neat," the child burst out delightedly. People were always getting after her about her hair being in disarray—it was fun to be able to tease Eliza.

To Polly's amazement, the usually tidy Eliza replied, "No matter. My face will soon cool off outside. I intend to cut greens and berries so we can dress the house."

Polly burst into giggles. Giving her sister an indulgent smile, Eliza asked, "Whatever is so comic about that, Mistress Roly-Poly?"

"You sound as if you are going to put a dress on the house!" Polly answered between giggles.

Eliza threw back her head in a merry laugh. "You little goose," she said affectionately. "That is what people call decorating a house with holly and greens. Nearly everyone in England does it at Christmas."

Noni, who was always getting separated from Polly, arrived at this moment to reclaim her charge, but Eliza sent the young nurse to the barn in search of Ezra.

Soon Ezra was busy cutting sprays of myrtle, whose glossy leaves glistened in the winter sun. Eliza next had him cut plenty of yaupon with its scarlet berrylike "drupes." These shrubs grew in the yard that surrounded the house. When the pile of sprays had grown nearly as large as she wanted, Eliza turned to a boy who had come from the barn with Ezra. He was one of the runners who carried food from the outside kitchen to the dining room in the house. "Sam, make haste to the quarters," she said, "and fetch two other boys to assist me."

While waiting for the boys, Eliza moved out to a pair of nearby holly trees and had Ezra cut as much red-berried holly as could be taken without damaging the trees.

The boys arrived on the run, and Eliza announced, "Now,

Ezra, we'll all go out to the big oaks beyond the barn. I saw bunches of mistletoe high in those trees."

Eliza admired the agility with which the boys climbed the tall trees. One of them crawled out on a limb and swung from it like a monkey. Another copied him, and soon they were competing in showing off. Polly squealed with pleasure, but Ezra shouted at the boys to get the mistletoe and come down. He was afraid they'd fall.

Together, the Lucas girls decorated the house with the greens and berries and showed Cully exactly where to hang the mistletoe at the entrances to the parlor and dining room.

Finally the great day came. Eliza, a naturally early riser, heard stirrings in the yard. She looked out to see all the Negroes of the plantation gathered around a big fire in the field nearest the house. Some of the boys who served as runners were posted in the yard, and when they saw Eliza at the window, they raced toward the house. They were the first to call out the traditional plantation greeting, "Christmas gift!"

Their cries proved the signal for the other Negroes to come pouring into the yard to repeat the greeting that was always said first on Christmas morning.

Eliza could hear her father call out from his window, "Merry Christmas to all of you."

Polly, always a late sleeper, had been awakened by the noise. Now she came running to add her greeting and to jump up and down in her excitement.

The father and his two daughters dressed rapidly and were soon on the porch. Major Lucas gave a cheerful Christmas greeting and then, in his ringing army voice, said, "Go and have a great big breakfast by the bonfire. There will be plenty to eat. After that come back for your presents."

Eliza asked Cully if he was certain there were enough

spareribs being roasted. He assured her that there was more than enough of all kinds of hog meat and other food as well.

After their own breakfast, Eliza threw her cloak around her and helped Polly into hers. They returned to the rear porch of the house. Major Lucas was already issuing the customary Christmas dram of rum to each of the men, as well as their present of tobacco.

Eliza and Polly joined him in presenting the other gifts. The last present to be given out was the fiddle and bow for Cully. A grin of delighted surprise spread across Cully's face, and he was voluble in his thanks. He immediately tucked the fiddle under his chin and played a gay little tune. The children broke into dance steps, and several older boys turned cartwheels in their exuberance.

No work was done that day except in the kitchen and "big house." Mrs. Woodward and Mrs. Chardon arrived for dinner with gifts in hand. Dressed in a pale green lutestring gown, whose glossy silk reflected the candlelight, Mrs. Lucas greeted her guests and graced the table for Christmas dinner. It was a smiling Cully who bore in the savory dishes his wife had prepared. The meal was as English as if it were being served in Oxfordshire.

After dinner, Eliza persuaded her father to play some military marches on his kettledrums. It was the first time he had done so since their arrival in South Carolina. Then everyone joined in singing Christmas carols, with Eliza playing the accompaniment on the harpsichord.

From the quarters, all day long, came the sounds of merriment. Late in the afternoon, after their guests had left and Mrs. Lucas had gone back to bed, Eliza and her father took a walk around the yard. From the big nursery house in the quarters, they could hear the music of Cully's new fiddle rising above the sound of feet sashaying to the gay tunes. The burdens of every day were forgotten—there was no sadness on Wappoo plantation that Christmas Day.

The new year of 1739 was ushered in at Wappoo by a warm spell that was in sharp contrast to the Christmas weather. Eliza asked her father if they could not now lay out the flower garden they had planned together. He was instant in his agreement and was soon at work with Ezra. They drove pegs and drew strings between them to outline the shape of the borders. Each bed was in a precise geometric shape. Major Lucas took great satisfaction in seeing that the design was made exactly like the sketch he and Eliza had drawn on paper.

Ezra, who had looked after the Lucas garden in Antigua, was obviously pleased to be back at his regular work. He dug and spaded with a will and pulverized the soil as if it were to be made into a pudding. Wiping the sweat from his brow, Ezra boasted to a young helper about the fine flowers they would raise at Wappoo.

As she and her father walked around the future garden, Eliza pointed out where they would have flowering catalpa trees. Roses would be in the center circle and pansies around the edges of the borders, which would contain sweet William, pinks, bell-shaped campanulas, and phlox.

"Mrs. Deveaux," Eliza told Major Lucas, "has promised to separate some of her lilies for me, and Mrs. Woodward has many plants and cuttings she is going to give us. And each has promised to tell me the proper time for planting."

Once the garden was laid out, Eliza felt she could spare time to put her clothes in order for the coming visit to the Pinckneys. She was consumed with excitement at the prospect. When the day came, Major Lucas took Eliza to Charles Pinckney's law office in Charles Town as agreed. While listening to her father saying good-by to Colonel Pinckney, Eliza experienced a sudden wave of panic. Why had she ever agreed to go for a visit with almost total strangers? Her throat constricted, and she had a wild desire to say she felt ill and must return to Wappoo with her father. But then Eliza noted her father's calmness and felt ashamed of herself. He would not be sending her on this visit if he had not thought it would prove enjoyable to her.

Charles Pinckney at once escorted Eliza to his carriage. He instructed his coachman to tuck the laprobe under Eliza's feet so she would be snug and warm. It was not long before her host's kind manner had chased away Eliza's fright. As he turned from closing the carriage window nearest her, Eliza studied his face. She decided that Colonel Pinckney was a handsome man—not in a classical way, but big and rugged and very masculine. Never had she seen a face that combined such kindness with so much strength. No wonder that he was trusted by the people of South Carolina and the governor, too!

Charles Pinckney interrupted Eliza's thoughts by speaking of the dance he and his wife were going to give in her honor. "Cephas says his fiddling arm is in good shape again, so I think the music will be merry enough to set the feet tripping. Mrs. Pinckney has rounded up many young people for the affair. Some will come down from Goose Creek district, and they will stay the night with us."

Eliza listened intently to her host as he continued talk of the coming dance. She was about to ask a question when she caught sight of the Pinckney's plantation home.

"Oh, how handsome Belmont is!" she exclaimed enthusiastically. "I do like a brick house. They always seem so solid and reliable. Do you not agree?"

Colonel Pinckney chuckled. "Well, I am partial to them,

but our earliest houses here were of wood, mostly cypress, and, if protected from fire, will last longer than you or I."

"Now I can see the fine creek on the far side of the house," Eliza said with rising excitement. "It flows into the Cooper River, doesn't it?"

"Yes, if it were not quite so late in the afternoon, you could see the river right over there," replied Colonel Pinckney, pointing downstream.

That evening there were no other guests, and this pleased Eliza; she was eager to become better acquainted with the Pinckneys. After a lavish tea, Mrs. Pinckney proposed a game of loo. When a few games had been played, however, Colonel Pinckney rose, declaring, "I think we would enjoy each other's conversation more than cards."

Eliza thought so, too, for she was brimming with questions she was eager to ask. Her host was soon highly amused by her serious interest in the crops raised on his plantation. But Eliza had grown accustomed to that kind of reaction and did not let it stop her inquiry. "Colonel Pinckney, I have been trying to find someone who grows indigo or has tried it," she said. "Tell me, have you raised it at Belmont?"

Charles Pinckney's eyes widened at the question. "Indigo —why no, I have never raised it. No one has yet successfully produced the dye from plants raised here, so far as I know," he replied. "With my law practice and official duties, Mistress Eliza, I fear I raise only the tried and true crops and leave the experimenting to others. But how did you happen to ask?"

" 'Tis probably just a silly conceit of mine, but I think it would be such a splendid crop for the dry ground on Carolina plantations, as rice is in the low, swampy areas. I learned a little of indigo culture from Papa after he visited Montserrat last summer. He told me how they raise it there and how they make the dye, and I thought some planter here must be succeeding with it."

Charles Pinckney's reply was courteous but showed plainly that he thought previous efforts had proved conclusively that indigo could not be successfully raised in South Carolina.

Observing Eliza's disappointment at this answer, Mrs. Pinckney quickly steered the conversation to talk of the coming dance. Colonel Pinckney spoke of the guests who had accepted their invitation and told Eliza interesting things about them. "I tell you about our friends," he added, "because I myself always find it more enjoyable to meet new people when I know a bit about them."

The next evening, when Eliza met the Pinckneys' guests, she found them just as attractive as Charles Pinckney had led her to believe. They soon made her feel one of them. Gone was the concern that had disturbed Eliza the preceding night —she was not in the least tongue-tied at meeting so many strangers.

The Pinckneys' house was aglitter with candlelight. The soft glow reflected on well-polished silver and highly waxed floors. When the dancing began, Eliza felt she could dance all night. She very nearly did for it was almost dawn when the last guest left. One dashing young man from Charles Town told her, "You dance as light as a down feather on the wind." It was but one of many compliments Eliza received that night, but she tried to remember her father's warning not to take flattery too seriously.

When the time came, Eliza found it hard to leave Belmont, but an invitation to return eased her departure, and her regrets melted away when her father met her in Charles Town and took her back to Wappoo. Polly was on the dock waiting for her with a barrage of questions. Eliza gave her sister an affectionate hug before answering her. "Yes, Polly, every minute at Belmont was delightful. The Pinckneys treated me like a fully grown lady. In fact, Colonel Pinckney made me feel like a princess, he was so courtly in his manners. And fancy this—he talked to me about books and government and even the laws of South Carolina."

Polly made a face. "I would rather talk about my pony, or our dog's new puppies, than those things," she said rather crossly.

"Yes, of course you would, lamb," Eliza replied. "But 'tis different for me. Papa likes me to learn such things. And, Polly, Colonel Pinckney said I had 'a lively spirit and a questing mind.'"

That was one compliment that Eliza had obviously taken seriously, but Polly thought little of it. All she said was, "Grown people really do say funny things." She was not through with her questions yet and asked eagerly, "Is their house bigger than ours?"

"Oh yes, much larger and such a handsome library. Colonel Pinckney lent me some books to bring home, and Mrs. Pinckney gave me a receipt that will teach me to cook terrapin the way she does."

Once inside the house and alone, Polly grinned up at her sister and teasingly asked, "Was Rob Leicester there?"

Eliza blushed. "Yes, he was," she admitted. "In some ways, you are older than your years, you tease. There was an exceedingly pretty girl from the Goose Creek area who seemed fair smitten with Rob."

Talk of Rob interested Polly. She snuggled closer to her sister and said, "Go on, go on. Did he dance more times with you or that other girl?"

"Oh, Polly, you shouldn't ask such things," Eliza said, but

her tone was not very convincing. She laughed happily and then continued, "Let us just say Rob danced often with me. The music set my feet tapping."

But Polly could be persistent, and she had come to like Rob on his visits to Eliza. Her eyes were very big as she asked solemnly, "Did Rob dance with you a hundred times?"

"How you do go on about Rob! He is a handsome young man, but his conversation does not hold a candle to Colonel Pinckney's," Eliza declared with some vehemence. She tossed her head and walked away from Polly to avoid any further questions.

As Eliza settled in again to her home duties, she thought often of each happening at Belmont. It had been a lovely, carefree holiday that she knew she would always remember.

At breakfast one morning, not long after her return, Major Lucas said to Eliza, "I have ordered my overseers—both Murray at Garden Hill plantation and Starrat at the Waccamaw property—to bring all their accounts up to date." Rising from the table, he paced up and down the room as he continued. "I think I had best tell you, Eliza, I heard yesterday that the outlook for peace between England and Spain has worsened. So, I must put my affairs in order. If I have to return to my regiment, you will need to know all possible about the three plantations, especially where each stands financially."

Eliza's heart ached for her father. She had never seen him so worried before. She rose and went to his side and laid her hand on his arm in reassurance. "Papa, dear," she said, "I know I am small of stature, but that does not mean I am frail. I am strong enough for any responsibility you may ask me to carry."

Major Lucas leaned down so that his face was on a level with hers. Solemnly and slowly he said, "I believe you are, my brave little Betsey."

Eliza's eyes misted with tears, and there was a lump in her throat. Her father had not called her "Betsey" for so long. It had been a very special pet name he had used for her as a child and one she had never allowed anyone else to employ. They could call her Eliza, as she called herself, though christened Elizabeth.

In the next weeks Major Lucas redoubled his efforts to complete the clearing of two more fields. The grubbing out of roots and the burning of tree stumps were slow processes, but he kept his men at the work throughout the daylight hours. At night he settled to his desk and worked on the Wappoo accounts.

Early one sunny winter morning, when he was taking his prebreakfast walk, Major Lucas discovered that the Wappoo dock needed repairing. All the nails having been used up on the repairs to the barn and cabins, he dispatched the patroon in a pettiauger to Charles Town, with instructions to buy some nails and extra tools.

Eliza was just dismounting after her morning ride when she saw the patroon return from his trip into town. He carried what he had bought in a sack swung over his shoulder. In his right hand he held several letters. She took the mail and hurried to her father's library, where Major Lucas was working at his desk.

"Papa," Eliza said, "Jethro is back from Charles Town with the purchases, and he brought this packet of letters for you off a schooner just arrived from Antigua. Mr. Millington entrusted them to him."

At those words Major Lucas rose, seized the proffered

mail, and hastily scanned the outside of each letter. He tore open one, murmuring, "This is from Lieutenant Colonel Morris. It is an official communication."

Eliza noticed that her father's hands shook just a little, though he managed to control the expression of his face.

He looked up from the letter. "This is the word I hoped I would not receive, Eliza," he said in a choked voice. "Peace negotiations with the Spanish have broken off. Morris has been authorized to inform me that I must return at once to my post of duty with the regiment. The Duke of Marlborough, our regimental commander, has ordered the 38th Foot to be brought up to war strength immediately."

Eliza reached up and threw her arms about her father's neck. She could only murmur, "Oh, Papa dear," as she struggled to choke back sobs.

Major Lucas stroked his daughter's hair gently and then turned aside to file the letters in a case on top of his desk. It was typical of him, Eliza thought, that, in this moment of receiving news that would alter their lives completely, her father did not fail to follow his systematic ways. She knew he did it to cover the intensity of his feelings.

Major Lucas sat down again at his desk. "Eliza," he said, "send for Jethro to come in. I must dispatch a message immediately to the captain of the schooner. I have to secure a passage on his return trip to Antigua."

Very late that afternoon the weary patroon returned with word from Magnus Watson, master of the schooner, *Brother's Endeavor*. Captain Watson said he would be able to take Major Lucas as a passenger on his return voyage to Antigua, but the schooner would not leave for a good three weeks. A storm had damaged his main mast on the way up. Captain Watson's roughly scrawled note advised that the schooner would have to lie up for this repair and the fitting of two new sails.

Major Lucas frowned at news of the delay, but there was nothing he could do about it. Now he wrestled with a worse problem—how to break the news to his wife.

Six

Eliza lay rigid in her bed—tense with emotion. But, at least, she was alone with her thoughts and could admit to herself just how scared she was. Her head throbbed with questions. Could she possibly run the three plantations? Would the men accept orders from her? What if her mother's health grew worse? Could she take care of Mrs. Lucas and teach Polly, too? One question followed on another, and she found no answer to any of them.

Realizing that her mouth was as dry as flannel, Eliza rose to get a glass of water. As she raised the pitcher from the washstand, she heard her father pacing nervously back and forth in the downstairs hall.

The sound filled Eliza with contrition. She was shocked to realize she had been thinking only of herself and what she had to face. It mortified her that she had not felt more concern for her father with his far more serious problems. Kneeling down by the side of her bed, Eliza said a heartfelt prayer for strength and unselfishness. When she rose, she felt better able to meet the future.

Sleep was a long time coming, but Eliza had won her battle—never would she let her father know that she had doubted her ability to carry on in his absence.

Immediately after breakfast the next morning, Major Lucas said to Eliza, "Leave your usual inspection of the nursery and sick house in the quarters until later in the day. I want you to come to my library for a talk."

The major found it hard to begin. "Eliza," he finally said, "I have tried to train you as a soldier's daughter, to face situations no matter how grave. You know that I have preferred you to study nature and books rather than fritter your time on embroidery and idle chatter. Now, I have to put on your shoulders a burden that no other girl I know could carry." He sighed and looked searchingly at his daughter.

"Papa, Mr. Millington will advise me about managing the plantations," Eliza assured him quickly. "Pray remember that, as your agent, he had charge of all three of your places before we came here from Antigua."

Major Lucas frowned and rose to pace back and forth. "Yes, my dear, Mr. Millington will assist you, but it is now necessary that these plantations produce a profit that they never did under his management."

Eliza was puzzled. What lay behind those words?

"Papa, dear," she said pleadingly, "something is burdening you terribly. Please trust me with it. Tell me your worry. 'Tis not right you should bear it alone. I love you so, and there's nothing I would not do for you and Mama." Her voice and the expression of her face were both earnest and appealing.

Major Lucas sat down across the desk from his daughter. "Yes, I suppose I must tell you," he said reluctantly. "The fact is, Eliza, I have more land than money. You well know that my army pay is not large, nor are my sugar lands in Antigua and the small refinery big enough to yield much profit."

Eliza nodded in acknowledgment.

"Whenever a landowner stays away, crops are usually meager," Major Lucas continued. "Millington did the best he could for me here, but so far these three plantations have been more of a drain than a profit. Then there was your schooling in England, and now the boys are there. The medical care of your mother has been constant for some years and our move here, with the transportation of our belongings and people, strained my finances to the limit."

Major Lucas fell silent. Then with a visible effort he resumed. "In order to do all this, Eliza, I placed a mortgage on this plantation with my friend Charles Dunbar in Antigua. My army pay will never be sufficient to cover the mortgage and my regular expenses. So, what is disturbing me is that I leave you with the *necessity* of developing some crop that will produce handsome revenues. If that can be done, I can lift the mortgage and we can forge ahead to prosperous days. Mind you, I do not mean that we are impoverished, but I deem it fair for you to know that you and I have heavy payments to meet." His long, painful speech was over.

Eliza jumped up and ran around the desk to her father. She leaned lovingly against his shoulder. "Oh, Papa, so that is all that's worrying you," she declared cheerfully. "I thought the doctor must have told you on his last visit that Mama has some dread disease. Of course, we can make the plantation earn money and pay off that mortgage. I am so glad you told me. We two will work together toward our secret aim. You will write from Antigua, and I will supervise everything here just as you want it done."

Her youthful enthusiasm cheered her worried father. He could not help but laugh. "Eliza, you are a caution. I fear me you little suspect how hard it is to feed and clothe all our people, eighty-six in number, besides their children, not to mention the wages I must pay Murray and Starrat and then Farquharson in Antigua. Still, we own much land, and I refuse to yield to gloom as long as I have you for my right arm."

A man of action by nature, Major Lucas set promptly to showing Eliza how to keep ledgers for the three plantations, as well as the letter book in which copies of the orders written to Murray and Starrat were recorded.

He explained to her that Indian corn was to be planted in one of the newly cleared fields and field peas in the other. Then he asked Eliza what queries she had for him. She bombarded him with questions.

As they walked back to the residence after an inspection of the "new" fields, Major Lucas announced, "Eliza, I feel I simply must visit our other plantations before I leave the country. Captain Watson's delay for repairs may prove a blessing in disguise. It is vital that I inspect the place on the Waccamaw. 'Tis hard to see why Starrat cannot produce more out of those 2,950 acres. I have arranged to hire a small fishing vessel to sail me directly there. 'Twould take too long to ride by land, for 'tis a good eighty miles northeast of here."

"Yes, Papa, I think you are most wise to go," Eliza replied.

"If your mother will consent," Major Lucas announced suddenly, "I propose to take you with me, since you will have to manage the work there. Once you have seen the property, you can more intelligently issue instructions to Starrat."

Eliza gave her father a joyful hug. She was thrilled at the prospect. How adventurous to go sailing off in a small boat to the rather undeveloped country to the north!

Major Lucas's Waccamaw plantation lay well to the northeast of the Huguenot homes on the Santee River, even beyond the new settlement of Georgetown. "Practically virgin soil," Major Lucas commented as he inspected the fields.

"There is richness here." He scooped up a handful of earth and said, "I wonder if this place would not grow indigo, Eliza. I should think it could—not the swampy land but the higher dry ground. And I feel the same about Wappoo." He rubbed his chin thoughtfully before adding, "We will certainly have to try for some new cash crop."

Back at the Wappoo plantation, Major Lucas and Eliza rested a few days before setting off southward to visit their Garden Hill plantation on the Combahee River. They found the overseer, Murray, proud of running the 1,500-acre place. Eliza made friends with the man and his wife and extracted from them the promise of regular reports.

When the Lucases were leaving, Murray remarked, "I am glad you have brought Sogo back. He is the only cooper I have to make the barrels for shipping the rice."

In the Wappoo neighborhood, word spread of Major Lucas's impending departure for Antigua. Several neighbors came to say that they would try to help Eliza and would look out for the safety of Mrs. Lucas and the girls.

From Charles Town Charles Pinckney arrived by petti-auger to offer Major Lucas any assistance he could give to the ladies during the major's absence.

Visibly moved, Major Lucas bowed low. "The kindness of you Carolinians has quite overwhelmed me," he declared. "I can leave now without a sense of dread about my family. It gives me a great sense of assurance, Colonel Pinckney, that you will keep an eye on my household of ladies."

After Major Lucas's departure, his wife had to go back to bed. For the days preceding his sailing, she had dressed daily, acted in her old gay manner, and given her husband a sense that she was infinitely stronger. The effort had sent him off in cheerful spirits but had taken a great toll of the delicate woman.

Now Eliza was busy from rising until bedtime attending to details of housekeeping, adding to the planting in the garden borders, and supervising the whole work of the plantation.

It was time for rice planting in the marshland. Eliza consulted carefully with her neighbors to be sure that she was having it done just the way they did. She promptly ran into a difficulty she had feared. Solomon, who had served as a foreman of the field hands under Mr. Millington and been continued in that capacity by Major Lucas, obviously found it hard to accept orders from a sixteen-year-old girl. The stalwart slave did not actually defy her, but he was extremely slow in carrying out her instructions.

This vexed Eliza as she was striving for maximum production from the Wappoo acres. Fortunately, she was able to hide her annoyance. It was a situation, she realized, that would eventually change if she proved able in her management.

One source of comfort to Eliza was that she could virtually turn over the planting of the vegetable garden to Ezra. And she could count on him to care for the flower borders in the yard without her telling him.

When plantation difficulties crowded too hard on her, Eliza went into the woods, where the birds were ecstatic over the arrival of spring. In describing them to her mother, Eliza called the song birds her "airy choristers." Her other great source of delight was the luxuriance of spring blooms at Wappoo and the delicious perfume of the wild honeysuckle. She loved the creeping white flower of the partridge berry that grew under trees. Eliza took to strolling near the creek where grew the plant called virgin's-bower, handsome with stiff purple petals. Later she found blue flags growing in watery places. In her planted borders, flowers reared their heads, and Eliza wrote of this with pride to her far-off father.

With the refreshment she derived from nature, Eliza was able to keep up her courage and her determination. She got the Indian corn planted on time.

Perhaps the most astonished of her field hands were the men assigned to "slash and box" the pine trees to catch the turpentine that dropped from the cut. The men had little thought that Eliza would show up in the pine woods to watch their work, but she did.

Rob Leicester came to call twice, but Eliza found it hard to be gay and social when she had not yet mastered her new responsibilities. She tried to make "parlor talk" but succeeded poorly, and each time she was relieved when Rob left early.

Every Sunday Eliza rode to St. Andrew's with Polly by her side and Ezra as their protector. But during the week she cut her outside activities to a minimum. When Mrs. Woodward demurred, Eliza explained that soon she would manage more easily and be able to resume social life.

Mr. Deveaux came over every week to see how Eliza was getting along. "Mistress Eliza," Mr. Deveaux urged, "have the women pick mustard greens and cress to cook with their pork. We find that builds up their health and helps ward off the intermittent fevers, or country fever, as some prefer to call it."

There were not enough hours in the day for the busy girl. Eliza was getting up at five every morning, but even so, her day was not long enough for her to give sufficient time to Polly. She had cut the child's lessons to a minimum. This worried Eliza and Mrs. Lucas, but Eliza assured her mother she could soon again lengthen the teaching.

Polly was delighted to escape classes and took to playing around the landing on the creek. Since Noni was scared of water, she was forever dragging Polly away from that fascinating spot. So, Eliza arranged to have Jethro, the patroon, take Polly and one of his youngsters out with him whenever he went fishing. Fish were so abundant in the creek and in the Ashley River that Polly herself sometimes caught a fish on the line she dangled. Whenever this happened, she was beside herself with joy and rushed to the kitchen to demand that the fish be specially prepared for her mother.

Seven

On the first day of July, Eliza, who was out inspecting the stable, was pleased to have a runner come after her with the message that Colonel Pinckney was calling at the "big house."

Charles Pinckney was his usual charming self and did much to brighten Mrs. Lucas with accounts of the festivities that were going on in Charles Town. Many of the planters had gathered there to get away from the swamp country and drink in the fresh clean air of the Atlantic Ocean.

Just before he left, Charles Pinckney walked out in Eliza's new flower garden with her. He was complimentary about her progress with the borders. "I must send you some of our fine sour orange trees. You will have a nice spot here for an orangery," he declared.

Eliza smiled with delight and thanked him. "I so much want to have fruit," she said. "We were accustomed to it in Antigua." Then, since they were out of hearing of the house, she asked, "Sir, is there any news of fighting with the Spanish? I can reach no conclusions from what I read in the *Gazette*."

Colonel Pinckney lowered his rich full voice when he replied, "I did not wish to alarm your mother, but I have again had news from my friend, the judge in London," he said gravely. "You may recall my speaking of him to your father.

He advises me that Admiral Edward Vernon is equipping his fleet in a way that indicates war. The admiral is yet in the home waters of Great Britain, or at least he was, but my correspondent implied that Vernon's departure might be imminent."

Eliza let out a gasp. "My, that does sound as if war is almost here." With great effort she controlled her voice and asked Colonel Pinckney a question. "Did my father ever speak to you of the efforts he has been making to exchange his commission as a major of the 38th Regiment of Foot in Antigua with Major Heron who holds a similar commission in the forces here on the mainland under General Oglethorpe?"

"He merely mentioned that he was negotiating for it and that he had left the matter in the hands of an agent named Bensby. 'Tis a mortal shame it could not have been arranged before your father left here," Charles Pinckney replied. "I bear the title of colonel in our militia, but, unfortunately, I have no military contacts through which I can assist your father. It does seem as though the British army could transfer Major Lucas to duty in Georgia, or one of our neighboring colonies, during your mama's illness."

"I wish it were so, for Major Heron won't exchange unless Papa pays him a large sum to do it."

Charles Pinckney started to reply, but Ezra was approaching, trundling a barrow up the sandy path, so the colonel dropped the subject. "Tell me, Mistress Eliza, are you keeping up your study of French?" he asked genially.

"My work has not lately permitted it, but I greatly enjoy trying to sing songs in that lovely language," replied Eliza. "Sometimes I make such a clatter, I think I frighten the mockingbirds who have a nest just outside the parlor window."

She laughed softly, and Charles Pinckney chuckled.

"You told me your father was going to send you some seeds from the West Indies. Have you received them?" Colonel Pinckney inquired.

"No, we have had almost no mail. But I believe Papa will send them by autumn, especially indigo seed. I am eager to try to raise indigo and make dye from it."

Charles Pinckney looked hard at Eliza to see if she could really be serious. He hated to think of the disappointment she was inviting. Knowing that he could always capture Eliza's interest by a discussion of books, he asked her opinion of one he had recently lent her. After an animated discussion, Colonel Pinckney said, "Your company is most delightful, but I see by the sun that I must return to town. If ever you feel you can come in for some gaiety, do remember our standing invitation to you."

Colonel Pinckney's discussion of her interests was like a tonic to Eliza. She returned straight from seeing him off at the dock to her father's desk in the library. Dipping a quill pen into the ink, Eliza began a letter to Major Lucas.

As she folded the sheets, she wondered how long it would be before she would receive a reply from her papa. She so desperately longed for answers to the questions she had written him.

Mrs. Lucas was pleased when a note came one hot late summer day urging Eliza to come in to Charles Town for a visit to the Pinckneys. She took the note from Eliza's hand and read it out loud in her thin, tired voice:

There is to be a concert on Wednesday next and I wish you to attend with Mr. Pinckney and myself. I pray you to give us the pleasure of your company. Mr. Pinckney says, "Tell the only young lady planter in South Carolina that diversion is part of a planter's life."

Mrs. Lucas smiled as she laid the letter on the candle stand by the side of her bed. "They are indeed charming people. I shall insist that you go, Eliza. I cannot have you bury yourself in work. Why even the men do not work as you do! Colonel Pinckney is quite correct in his statement."

Eliza laughed merrily. "No, the men do not," she admitted. "But they do not have so much to learn about running plantations as I do. However, Mama, I should dearly love to go to the concert. Since you want me to do so, I will arrange to attend to my business with Mr. Millington at that time. That will kill two birds with the one stone."

Dancing gaily to her mother's bedside, Eliza kissed her on the forehead. "To be truthful, Mama, I can scarce wait to go," Eliza said as she retrieved the note from Mrs. Lucas's hand.

"Jethro brought word from the mantuamaker that your new sprigged dimity would be ready Friday. Oh, I am so pleased I insisted you have one made, Eliza. That will be cool and look charming on you at the concert," Mrs. Lucas announced with satisfaction.

When Eliza attended the musical event in Charles Town, there were many who did in truth find the sprigged dimity most becoming to the slight girl with the expressive large eyes.

The concert was given by a group of musicians who had the winter before played for the Royal Governor of Virginia at the palace in Williamsburg. The real feature of the evening, though, was the singing of an Italian tenor, late of Covent Garden Theater in London and now on his way to New York and Philadelphia.

Rob Leicester had spied Eliza arriving with the Pinckneys and quickly came to her side during the intermission. He murmured a compliment on her charming appearance and said, "Miss Eliza, pray set the date when I can come to Wappoo to sing some more to your accompaniment. If you were more generous with my training, perhaps you could bring me nearer to the easy voice of the artist tonight."

Mr. Izard, a white-haired gentleman from the Goose Creek district, who had taken a fancy to Eliza at the Pinckneys' dance for her, broke into the conversation. " 'Pon my word, young lady, you look fresh as a daisy. No sign of intermittent fever about you, I'm glad to say. And now I must deliver a message—Charles Pinckney thought you might wish to hear the news Rhett Broughton has just brought from London."

"Indeed, I would. Where is Mr. Broughton?" Eliza asked eagerly.

Mr. Izard nodded to a cluster of men gathered at the far end of the room. He offered his arm to Eliza, and they made their way toward the group. Rob Leicester followed, but his face showed his displeasure over the interruption that had ended his conversation with Eliza.

When the three reached the cluster gathered around Rhett Broughton, Charles Pinckney stepped forward to introduce Eliza and Mr. Broughton. "Rhett, pray repeat to Miss Lucas the war news you've just told us. It will be of profound interest to her as her father is on army duty in Antigua."

Rhett Broughton turned to Eliza. "On July 19, Admiral Vernon received orders to open hostilities against Spain. He was in home waters then, and in four days' time he set sail for the West Indies."

A murmur ran through the assembled listeners. There were many questions, but the musicians were again tuning up their violins, and the manager of the concert passed among the guests, urging them to take their seats.

Eliza tried to control a trembling that had come over her at the news. The British fleet had sailed for the West Indies. That meant there would be action and her father would be involved. She felt drained of hope—hope to which she had clung—that her father would still be exchanged with an officer on duty in the American colonies. There was no use holding that dream any longer. Fighting tears, Eliza tossed her head back and cocked her chin resolutely. She must not fail her father.

Eight

The wind had freshened and was blowing straight out of the east. Eliza, standing on the high bank of Wappoo Creek, breathed deep of the cool sea air. It bore a delicious promise of autumn to come. She closed her eyes and let the wind caress her face. It was so good to realize that the intense steamy heat of the summer was over. Now there would be fewer mosquitoes. Now surely her mother's recurring bouts of "chills and fever" would cease. She and Polly had been lucky. They had had only light touches of the intermittent malarial fever that was the plague of the hot months.

For the hundredth time, Eliza rejoiced that their Negroes had kept so well. She had had only minor doctoring to do, and Otelia, who served as midwife in the sick house in the quarters, had without difficulty delivered two fine babies. The general good health of the workers, Mr. Deveaux had told Eliza, was due to the balanced diet she had supplied them. They had been provided with an abundance of cabbage, onions, carrots, potatoes, beets, and turnips and generous quantities of fresh beef during the summer now ending. The vegetables had been made possible by Ezra's success with the large garden plot.

It was Sunday morning, and, as usual, Eliza was waiting for Polly to be ready to leave for church. Eliza was impatient to be off because she was pressing toward the time when she could talk to Mrs. Woodward after the service at St. Andrew's. In spite of Polly's dawdling about her dressing and the long sermon that the Reverend Mr. Guy preached that morning, the time finally came when the congregation poured out of the church. Eliza quickly joined Mrs. Woodward and Mrs. Chardon. She greeted them affectionately and, without any further delay, plunged into what was on her mind. "How soon, Mrs. Woodward," Eliza asked eagerly, "will your overseer start your rice harvest?"

"Tomorrow morning. I knew I would see you at church, Eliza, or I would have sent a messenger to bring you word of it," Mrs. Woodward replied. "I have scarce forgot that you want to watch each step of the harvest. It is most intelligent of you. Your rice must be almost ripe, is it not?"

"It will be full ripe in five days, Solomon tells me," replied Eliza.

"Then you will be able to observe nearly the whole process at our plantation before you begin your own," remarked Mrs. Woodward kindly.

" 'Tis true, of course, that we have only one large rice field at Wappoo, but I do want to handle the harvest correctly. I feel so responsible with Papa far away."

"Eliza dear, we do understand and want to help in any way we can," Mrs. Chardon declared impulsively. "We will expect you to have midday dinner with us each day while you are observing the harvest methods."

During the next days, Eliza not only watched the rice harvest at her neighbor's but also asked many questions of Mrs. Woodward's experienced overseer.

On Friday morning Eliza dressed extra early. She had the night before given the order to start reaping the Wappoo rice. After enjoying two cups of hot chocolate and a roll, she made her way to the dirt bank surrounding the field of rice.

She felt a little catch in her throat as she gazed at the field of rice rippled by a gentle breeze. Mr. Deveaux had declared it "a fine stand of rice," and Eliza was proud of it. In the early September sunshine, the bowed heads of the grain looked like burnished gold. "Oh, how I wish Papa were here—'tis such a beautiful sight," Eliza murmured softly to herself. Seeing Solomon approach, she turned practical and gave the order to begin the reaping. The afternoon before, Eliza had made sure that all the reaping hooks had been sharpened on the grindstone.

The field hands moved into the swampy rice field swinging their short reaping hooks precisely but without strain. Eliza watched to be sure they were careful as they laid the long golden heads on the stubble of rice stalks. The next day she was back at the field to see the dried rice heads tied into sheaves and stacked neatly in small cocks. It was both relief and satisfaction to Eliza when the sheaves were carried to the barnyard and the process of flailing or beating the rice heads off the stalk began.

The flailing was a noisy business and one that seemed to fascinate Polly. Eliza told Noni to let Polly watch but to keep her out of the way of the workers.

Even after the threshing, the rice grains were still covered with their tough husks, the hulls. Eliza saved a quantity of this rough rice for seed and feed for cattle. The rest of the rice then had to be prepared for table use—the hull and bran layers being removed to leave the whole kernel for eating. When finally the work was finished, Eliza was a tired but happy girl. She estimated that the rice produced at Wappoo was enough to supply the plantation for the winter, with some extra to ship her father. Before long, Eliza received word from Murray and Starrat that they had produced fine yields of rice at the other two Lucas plantations. Eliza wrote both overseers that she wished three-fourths of the rice barreled at that time and sent by the plantation boat to Charles Town. In late October, when Eliza went into Charles Town to buy the woolen clothing for the slaves, Mr. Millington handed her an accounting sheet.

"You have managed well, Mistress Eliza," he declared with obvious pleasure. "The rice you have sent me settled your account for tools and other items I have supplied you for the three plantations, and there are many barrels left over to ship to England."

Eliza's first crop of Indian corn was also bountiful. There would be plenty of hominy to eat that winter. She could ship corn to her father and still have enough to grind into the meal used daily in the making of various kinds of corn-meal bread. White wheat flour, Eliza had early learned, was a luxury in South Carolina, for it was brought to Charles Town by coasting ships out of Philadelphia or Boston.

The good crops lifted a burden from Eliza's heart in that autumn of 1739—she had been so afraid of failing in the trust her father had committed to her. She longed to talk about it with someone close, but she had given up trying to discuss such things with her mother. Mrs. Lucas wasn't interested in plantation matters. Polly was too young to understand. And so, Eliza fell back on her pen. She wrote to her father and gave details of what she had done. She asked also when he would send the seeds and cuttings he had promised her. Now that she had learned how to handle the staple South Carolina crops, she was extremely eager to begin experimenting with new ones.

At last, Eliza felt sufficiently the master of her plantation management to spare time for other activities. She resumed her regular teaching of Polly each morning. In addition to Polly she had two new pupils—Otelia's young daughers. Impressed by the bright minds of these little girls, Eliza had sought and obtained her mother's permission to teach them to read, write, and figure. Eliza was far from a trained teacher, but her interest and her enthusiasm were catching. Book learning was difficult for the girls, but they were as eager to learn as Eliza was to teach, and gradually they made progress. To her amazement, Eliza found that some of the neighbors disapproved of teaching the young Negroes, but she ignored the criticism. Mrs. Woodward and Mrs. Chardon, who were both deeply religious women, encouraged Eliza with their approval.

For months Eliza had stifled her hunger for more personal pleasures. She was eager to go on with her study of music, one of her great enthusiasms. At this time Mrs. Chardon suggested that her own music master, Mr. Pelham, might be able to give Eliza lessons on the same day. This was arranged, and Eliza was happy as a lark to be improving both her harpsichord playing and her singing.

Rob Leicester came out from Charles Town for a few days of duck shooting with the Draytons and Eliza was invited to a duck feast at Drayton Hall. On another occasion she laced herself into her best tight-bodiced, hooped-skirt dress, donned her highest-heeled shoes, piled her hair high up on her head, and danced the night away at the Deveaux's hospitable home. They had gathered the immediate neighbors for the evening and had included Rob, who was liked by both Mr. and Mrs. Deveaux.

More attentive than ever, Rob declared that night, "Truly, Miss Eliza, you are a delight at every festive occasion. Providence surely never intended you to devote yourself to the serious matters of a plantation. Do come more often to Charles

Town. I confess I pine to see you as oft as is humanly possible."

"If I were to come often, would you carry out the promise you made me in the summer—to commence the study of law?" Eliza asked very seriously.

Rob laughed. "You are a charmer but a minx as well," he declared. "Yes, I will even chain myself to the law books if you insist. 'Twas like you to persuade Colonel Pinckney to say he would supervise my reading law in his office. Now I have no excuse not to do so—so I shall begin and try not to loathe it too much. But 'tis a vast price I pay, Miss Eliza."

Smiling up at him, Eliza asked. "How can you say 'tis such a price when you had planned earlier to go to London to study law at the Inner Temple?"

"True, I had while my father lived," Rob admitted. "But now it seems a dull waste of time. You know Lieutenant Governor Bull has received a request from General Oglethorpe to send troops from South Carolina to join the Georgia force in an attack on St. Augustine. No answer has been given yet. It would be such a glorious expedition. We in the militia are determined to have a chance to join it."

The smile vanished from Eliza's face, and her eyes clouded with worry. "So that is why you have not kept your promise," she said sadly.

"And what better reason, Mistress Eliza?" Rob bristled with vexation. "As an officer's daughter, surely you would be proud to see me fight the Crown's battle against the Spanish."

"It is for the very reason that my father is already fighting that battle, Mr. Leicester, that I am so loath to have you go off to the wars." Eliza's voice betrayed her agitation.

In his elation at the emotion she had expressed, Rob seized Eliza's hands in his. "Then, of course, my lovely one, I shall start my legal studies at once. I know your loyalty to the Crown would release me from that pursuit if the province should need my sword."

Eliza thought he sounded like a recruiting officer, but what could she say?

Some weeks later, on a brisk, clear December morning, Eliza was supervising Ezra in mulching the flower borders with pine needles when she heard a rider approaching at a gallop. She listened intently. That could only be Rob Leicester—no one else rode a horse like that! Eliza felt a warm glow of delight. Peeling off her gardening gloves, she ran out of the yard to meet Rob as he dismounted from Xerxes, his fiery stallion.

With an exaggerated flourish, Rob made a bow so deep that the hat he held in his right hand brushed the earth.

Eliza laughed merrily. "Aha, Mr. Leicester," she said, "I thought you were training to be a lawyer, not a courtier." She curtsied daintily to him.

"Pray do not mention the law! If it had not been for your feminine guile, I should never have begun its study, Miss Eliza. Just because Colonel Charles Pinckney is such a brilliant lawyer is no reason for you to expect him to turn me into one." Rob spoke half jokingly, half seriously.

"But surely you find the study interesting?" Eliza asked in surprise.

Rob groaned. "No, I cannot say it fascinates me. I am having to wade through a legal work that Colonel Pinckney quotes as if it were the Bible."

"What is its title?" Eliza asked with interest.

"To be precise, it is the twelfth edition, published last year in London, of Sir Edward Coke's work, *The First Part of The Institutes of The Laws of England; or, A Commentary upon Littleton,*" Rob replied disgustedly. "Fancy my sitting

A dress of Eliza Lucas Pinckney pictured here on her great-great-granddaughter, the late Josephine Pinckney, South Carolina novelist. The photograph was taken in 1923 in the garden of Miss Pinckney's Charleston home. *Courtesy of the owner, Thomas Pinckney, of Richmond, Virginia*

harles Town harbor and waterfront much as Eliza Lucas saw it on her arrival
here late in 1738. Bishop Roberts painted the scene, from which this engraving was
made, in 1739, just a few months after Eliza landed in South Carolina. *Courtesy
of the Print Room, New York Public Library*

t. Andrew's Church, where Eliza Lucas attended services during her life at Wappoo
lantation, 1738-1744. Her marriage to Charles Pinckney, on May 27, 1744, was
erformed by the rector of this parish, the Reverend William Guy. *From the orig-
nal painting by Charles Fraser, courtesy of Carolina Art Association, Gibbes Art Gallery,
harleston, S.C.*

Charles Pinckney (c. 1699-1758), hus[band]
of Eliza Lucas Pinckney. This portrait[, the last]
painted of Chief Justice Pinckney rela[xing]
at home. The pushed-back turban re[veals]
how closely his hair was cropped to [make]
more comfortable the wearing of a w[ig in]
court.

Harriott Pinckney Horry, wife of Col[onel]
Daniel Horry and only daughter of [Eliza]
Lucas and Charles Pinckney. The ori[ginal]
of this miniature was painted of Har[riott]
in her middle years. *Copy painted by [Emma]
Rutledge Felder and owned by Mrs. Fran[ck]
Stewart, by whose permission it is repro[duced]*

Charles Cotesworth Pinckney (1746-1[825],
eldest son of Eliza Lucas and Cha[rles]
Pinckney and a framer of the Constitu[tion.]
As a major-general, 1798-1800, he [com]
manded all United States military posts [and]
forces south of Maryland, as well as [those]
in Kentucky and Tennessee. Portrait b[y]
Benbridge. *Courtesy of Kennedy Gall[eries,]
Inc., New York*

Thomas Pinckney (1750-1828), son of Eliza Lucas and Charles Pinckney, from the miniature painted by Charles Fraser in 1818. Pinckney wears the uniform of a major-general, in which rank he commanded all United States troops in the southern half of the country throughout the War of 1812. *Courtesy of Carolina Art Association, Gibbes Art Gallery, Charleston, S.C.*

St. Philip's Church in Charles Town, where Eliza worshiped after her marriage to Charles Pinckney. The funeral of Charles Pinckney was held there in 1758, and he lies buried in the graveyard of the church. This engraving, published in *The Gentleman's Magazine,* London, in 1753, shows the second St. Philip's structure that in 1723 had replaced an earlier wooden building and was itself destroyed by fire in 1835, to be replaced by the present St. Philip's Episcopal Church on the same site. *Courtesy of The Museum of Early Southern Decorative Arts, Winston-Salem, N.C.*

The mansion house of Charles and Eliza Lucas Pinckney is seen on the extreme right of this detail of a line engraving by Samuel Smith, "A View of Charles-Town, The Capital of South Carolina, From An Original Picture Painted at Charlestown in the Year 1774" by the artist Thomas Leitch. Charles Pinckney started construction of this house early in 1745. On the extreme left may be seen St. Philip's Church. *Courtesy of The Museum of Early Southern Decorative Arts, Winston-Salem, N.C.*

Hampton Plantation, home of Harriott Pinckney Horry. Eliza Lucas Pinckney lived here with her daughter after the Revolution, and it was on this portico that Eliza and her daughter welcomed President Washington in 1791. *Photograph by Ronald Allen Reilly, Charleston, S.C.*

in that stuffy law office poring over that tome when Admiral Vernon is doubtless now attacking the Spanish in the Caribbean and Oglethorpe will surely soon march on St. Augustine."

Eliza could not hide her distress.

Rob was instantly contrite. "Forgive me. 'Twas wrong of me to bring that subject up again. Believe me, I am attempting to understand this book, but I have had to pester Colonel Pinckney for explanations. After all, Coke was perhaps the greatest Chief Justice England ever had. Is it surprising that I should find it difficult?"

Reaching in a pocket for a handkerchief with which to brush dust off his coat, Rob's hand touched something crackly. "Oh, my good friend, what a dunce I am," he said in embarrassment as he drew forth two battered letters from his pocket. "I came riding out here posthaste to bring these letters and forgot my mission in feeling sorry for myself."

He handed the letters to Eliza—one was addressed to her, one to her mother. Eliza's face lit up like a thousand stars. "Will you excuse me while I hasten with this letter to Mama?" she asked.

"Of course, and pray take time to read your father's to you. I'll walk Xerxes to the stable and have him rubbed down and watered," Rob said. "Do come soon to the parlor, though, as I must return to Charles Town before dark, and 'tis a seventeen-mile ride, as you well know."

When Eliza joined him in the parlor, she was bubbling with delight. "Papa writes that he has the promise of cuttings of the ginger plant," she announced. "An officer stationed in Jamaica is sending them to him, and Papa thinks he can send them to me for a planting in the early spring. And he is also sending me cotton and cassava roots to try. He says that cassava makes an excellent kitchen vegetable and, if grown in sufficient quantity, can also be used to feed horned cattle."

"I can see you are going to be busy experimenting," Rob said lamely.

Still much excited over the seeds and cuttings she was to receive, Eliza failed to notice the look of boredom that had spread across Rob's handsome face. She continued, "I am also to receive lucerne seed. That is a splendid grass for animals. I do so hope I can succeed with one of the four."

"I have never heard you speak of any of those. I thought it was indigo you wished to try here, Mistress Eliza," Rob said rather petulantly.

The words pricked Eliza's balloon of happiness. The smile vanished from her face. "Your recollection is correct," she said. "It is indigo I so desire to raise here, but Papa says that so far he has had no fortune in obtaining the tiny black seeds."

Eliza dropped her head in discouragement. What was the matter between her and Rob? Everything they said seemed to hurt one or the other.

In an effort to lighten the charged atmosphere, Eliza rose and went to her harpsichord. She played Rob's favorite tune. He sang a few bars but could not put his heart into it, so he went to the window and glanced up at the sun. "I think, Miss Eliza," he declared, "I had best get back to Charles Town and resume my study."

Both young people were miserable as they said good-bye.

At Christmas, Rob came out with gifts for Mrs. Lucas, Eliza, and Polly. He apologized, and Eliza did likewise. They skirted serious subjects and went for a long, exhilarating horseback ride. Then he laughingly challenged Eliza to a fast game of cards. After his departure, she told herself that all was once more well between them.

Eliza went into Charles Town in January of the new year for a brief visit to the Charles Pinckneys. There she learned that General Oglethorpe's estimate of the troops South Carolina should send him for the expedition against St. Augustine had been received in Charles Town. Rob avoided this subject when he took her to an evening of tableaux at the theater, but Eliza could see that he was seething with excitement over the prospect of military action.

On March 23, 1740, Oglethorpe himself came to Charles Town to confer with the governor and Assembly. It was from Colonel Pinckney that Eliza learned that South Carolina had agreed to raise a regiment of four hundred men to serve with General Oglethorpe for a period of four months. Eliza had scarcely returned home before Rob Leicester came galloping up in a glow of enthusiasm. Alexander Vander Dussen, of the Goose Creek section, had been chosen colonel to head the regiment, he reported with fervor.

"Francis Le Jau is to be the lieutenant colonel, Miss Eliza, and you know what a fine man he is," Rob said persuasively. "The most splendid news of all is that Charles Colleton has been appointed major, and he wants me to be one of his ensigns. 'Tis not a high post, but then I would even march there as a private to be part of the attack against St. Augustine."

Eliza's heart plummeted like a stone into a deep well. Somehow she managed a smile and said, " 'Tis a signal honor, Mr. Leicester, that you have been chosen as an officer. I do congratulate you on the distinction you have won."

Carried away with his own jubilation, Rob failed to notice Eliza's careful wording or her lack of enthusiasm. He plunged on. "Our expedition will win as much honor against the Spaniards as Admiral Vernon did last November in Panama when he captured Puerto Bello. I know you are proud of that British achievement, and I will give you something to be proud of too, I pledge you."

Eliza knew that it was hopeless to demur. A man so on fire with martial ardor could never understand that he did not have to win his spurs in battle to make her proud of him.

Rob soon began drilling on Charles Town Neck with the regiment that was to join Oglethorpe on the expedition against St. Augustine. He came as often as he could to Wappoo to see Eliza. Once again he was the dashing, happy Rob she had first met. Eliza began to feel that she had been wrong to urge the study of law upon him—it did not seem that he was cut out for it.

By March, Eliza also had a new happiness, but it was one about which she did not speak to Rob. She had finally received a packet of tiny black indigo seeds from her father. Determined to succeed if it was possible, Eliza had Solomon, Ezra, and Jeemy, her best hands, prepare the ground. Then she instructed them to make rows eighteen inches apart. She herself crouched down to tuck the first of the seeds in the earth. A girl with a very real faith in God, Eliza said a silent prayer for the success of her venture. Each day she visited the field to see if the seeds had sprouted, and when plants thrust through the earth, Eliza was ecstatic with joy. Polly could not understand why she was so excited and said, "You have made so many other things grow, Eliza. Why are you so happy about these scraggly little plants?"

Every day Eliza's hope for success soared higher. But on April Fool's Day she waked to feel a most unseasonable chill in the bedroom. Dressing, she rushed outdoors, and her eyes confirmed her fears. There had been a frost in the night. Holding her skirts high, Eliza ran to the field of indigo. The sight sickened her. The small tender plants had been burned black by the totally unexpected frost. Solomon, who had long before come to admire Eliza, joined her at this moment. He shook his head sorrowfully, proclaiming that he had never known a frost this late at Wappoo.

Comforted by Solomon, Eliza said immediately, "We will try again. It is not too late. Get the men and prepare the soil again. I will fetch some more of the seed. No frost can possibly now come to destroy this planting."

Day by day, Eliza grew more confident that this time she would succeed in growing indigo, and she wrote her father a glowing letter about the fine plants she had in the field. The shock was, therefore, all the greater for Eliza when early one May morning Solomon came to the door at breakfast time to tell her that the worms had gotten into the indigo and devoured most of the young plants. Eliza closed her eyes. Her expectations were shattered; she was close to despair. To a penny she knew what the plantations had yielded the preceding year and how much she could earn if she could only perfect the growth of indigo and make dye from it.

That night Eliza cried herself to sleep. Would she ever be able to achieve this goal she had set for herself? The desire to make indigo had become her great dream. Through it Eliza saw a way both to end her father's financial worries and make a patriotic contribution to South Carolina, the province that had given such a kindly reception to her and her family.

After this pitiful end to what had promised so brilliantly, Eliza wished over and over that she had never written her father until the seed had been gathered. Oh, how could she have boasted before she had achieved! Now she had only gotten her papa's hopes up in vain.

Before Rob and the other soldiers were due to sail to join General Oglethorpe, various festivities were planned in Charles Town to honor the regiment. In spite of her heartache about her indigo failure, Eliza went in to stay with the Millingtons and go to the affairs with Rob. He alternated between singing her praises and predicting the brilliant showing the Americans would make on the expedition against St. Augustine.

Eliza had not had a new gown made for the farewell ball, but she looked lovely anyway. In her heart there was a haunting sadness over all these fine young men going off to be shot at, and she wondered how many would return. Because of this she made a great effort to be gay. She was literally sparkling, and Rob could not take his eyes off her.

But the celebration was soon over and the day of departure arrived. The troops sang lightheartedly as they went on board the transports on May 9 and sailed away three days later. In the weeks that followed, Eliza realized what a place in her life Rob had come to occupy. She missed him badly. He had forced her to be gay and not so serious, and she knew that it had been good for her. Besides, there was so much sweetness in him. Why couldn't she have had more time with him? Had she been wrong to work so hard? Oh, why did he have to go off to war?

Nine

It had been hard enough for Eliza to have her father far away on military duty in England's war with Spain. Now as the summer of 1740 grew hotter, Eliza found herself waking in the night with worry because Rob Leicester had also gone off to face the guns of the Spanish. On one such night, she was sitting beside her window trying to catch a breath of cool air when a mockingbird, perched in a nearby tree, burst into song. The bird poured out a flood of ecstasy sufficient to split its throat. It reminded Eliza of the rich love song of a nightingale she had heard once in England. Responding to the pure beauty of the notes, Eliza felt concern fade away. A new surge of determination flowed through her.

Listening to the lovely songster, Eliza resolved that she must try to make things happier for her mother and Polly and that, to do so, she herself must be more cheerful. She would keep busier than ever, and that would drive away sorrow and even her concern over the third crop of indigo she had planted late in the spring after the worms had devoured the leaves of her second planting.

Early each morning, as soon as she had set the twenty adult workers of the plantation to their tasks for the day, Eliza took Polly for a ride. Polly loved these expeditions in the cool of the morning. When some young relatives came to visit Mr. and Mrs. Deveaux at Westpenny plantation, Eliza saw to it that Polly had as much fun with the children as was possible. At that time Eliza even relented on Polly's lessons, but otherwise she continued to teach her sister and the young Negro girls. Because of the summer heat, Eliza usually instructed her charges wherever she could find the most shade outdoors. There they could benefit from any breeze that was stirring. As a change from learning out of books, Eliza developed a game to teach the youngsters the names of the birds at Wappoo. Until she developed this "bird game," Eliza had never been able to interest Polly in her feathered friends. The indigo bird, Polly soon announced, was her favorite. "I like that deep blue color of the male bird," Polly announced when she chose it as her mascot. Then, puckering up her face, she asked, "Eliza, why couldn't the female indigo bird be blue, too? It's not fair that she isn't pretty. I don't like her brown top and sort of yellow-white bottom feathers."

This gave Eliza the chance to explain why the mother bird needed dull coloring so that she would not be seen when sitting on her nest of eggs.

At this time Eliza also began writing more frequently to her brothers, George and Tom Lucas, who were at school in England and living at Mrs. Boddicott's, just as she had. She had suddenly realized how badly they must be missing the family.

Remembering how eager Rob had been for her to do more frivolous things, Eliza set aside each Tuesday for a good long visit with Mrs. Chardon and Mrs. Woodward, her nearest neighbors. There she indulged, at last, in the embroidery that her father deplored. It made her feel a little guilty, but it gave Eliza a chance to chat and be gay with her friends. Sometimes she took Polly along so she could continue her struggle to make a pretty sampler.

A visit from Colonel Pinckney brought Eliza a new supply of books and a new interest. She had earlier mentioned to him how many records she had to keep. Now Charles Pinckney brought her a pamphlet about shorthand. He showed her the system he had used to take notes when studying law at the Inner Temple in London. The idea quite intrigued Eliza, and she resolved forthwith to start studying shorthand. It would save her so much time.

"As for this copy of *Plutarch's Lives,* Colonel Pinckney," Eliza declared, "I shall take good care of it. I fear 'twill take me many a month to absorb its learning, but then I shall hope to discuss it with you."

"I shall look forward to that, Mistress Eliza," Colonel Pinckney replied. "I myself find fascinating the study of the lives of men who have overcome difficulties and achieved great things."

"Does it seem to you, Colonel Pinckney, that it is the *overcoming,* rather than their fame, that gives great men their satisfaction?" asked Eliza.

"Indeed it does, Mistress Eliza," Colonel Pinckney replied. "And if I may be permitted to say so, I think you quite excel at overcoming difficulties gracefully."

A flood of scarlet spread across Eliza's face, and she found no words.

"There, there," Colonel Pinckney said kindly. "Your modest blush becomes you, and now let us talk of what concerns us so deeply—the war with Spain. I presume you have heard that an American regiment is being raised in the colonies to the north of us to accompany Admiral Vernon on a great expedition against the Spanish?"

"Yes, I heard mention of it, but no details," replied Eliza.

"Word reached Charles Town the other day that the Virginia troops are expected to sail in August. But the man who brought the news expressed doubt that they would get off that early," said Colonel Pinckney.

"Will Admiral Vernon then join General Oglethorpe in besieging St. Augustine?" Eliza asked hopefully.

"Oh no, Oglethorpe has a sufficient force for that. The admiral will be after a far greater prize. I do not know it for certain, but there is speculation that Vernon will seek to capture Cartagena. Because it is the chief port of the Spanish colonies in northern South America, 'tis a treasure chest, but for the same reason, it is heavily fortified."

"Oh," was all the answer Eliza could manage. Hope had soared within her that Admiral Vernon's forces would assure the success of the campaign in which Rob was taking part.

It was some weeks later when Eliza finally heard from Rob. She ripped open the travel-stained letter and felt her face glow as she read the warm sentiments and hopes for the future he expressed. With pride he described General Oglethorpe's force of two thousand men—Scottish highlanders and large numbers of Creeks and Cherokee Indians, as well as the South Carolina troops. Rob had already been engaged in action at the recapture of Forts Picolata and San Francisco de Pupa, and at the seizure of Fort Diego. And now Castillo de San Marcos, the great bastion in St. Augustine itself, was only three miles away. Though she dreaded to think of Rob involved in such danger, Eliza was, in spite of herself, caught by his excitement at the prospect of battle, and she wondered again if she had been right to try do dissuade him from going. The letter closed with tender expressions of admiration.

From that moment Eliza walked on air until a day late in that summer of 1740 when Mr. Millington came by pettiauger to Wappoo. One look at the factor's face told Eliza he had come to report serious trouble. "What is it," she almost shouted. "Has Papa been wounded?"

"No, Mistress Eliza," Mr. Millington said kindly. "I came to tell you that General Oglethorpe's troops failed to capture St. Augustine and were forced to retreat. The Spanish had strengthened the walls of the fort and driven thousands of stakes into the ground outside. Those stakes had sharpened points to impale our men. It was a fearful objective to try to take."

But Eliza, her face drained of color, did not hear Mr. Millington's last words.

"You have come to tell me about Rob," she said in a voice icy with fear.

"Yes, my dear, I have. Rob Leicester died heroically," Mr. Millington said. "He charged into a withering fire when others were dropping back. You can be proud he was your friend."

Somehow Eliza moved through the next weeks. The management of the plantations had to go on. She daily inspected the field of indigo, but even her enthusiasm for that was dimmed. Mrs. Lucas and Polly had to be cared for. She worked at her study of shorthand but found it more difficult than ever. It was well that Eliza kept busy, for this was her first experience with grief.

One day Mrs. Chardon said to her very gently, "My dear, I loved my husband and I lost him. Well do I know that sorrow. You are so stricken that I must ask you—were you betrothed in secret to Rob Leicester?"

"Oh no, but he meant much to me. I am too young to think of marriage yet. I believe Rob cared for me, but he was too much of a gentleman to speak to me without Papa's permission. We disagreed about many things, but I loved every minute with him—he was my dearest friend," Eliza said with a choke in her voice.

"Then you must be friend to many others and not stay so secluded at Wappoo," replied Mrs. Chardon.

While Eliza could not quickly slough off her grief over Rob's death, she went about more in the neighborhood and invited friends in for tea.

She even grew hopeful about the third attempt she had made in that year of 1740 to grow indigo. The seed was drying nicely, Mr. Deveaux told her when he came to have a look at it. But the next morning her hopes were shattered. Though it was only mid-September, a freak early frost had struck in the night.

"Quick, Solomon, get Jeemy and Ezra. We must pick out all of the seed that is not ruined."

Eliza turned aside to keep Solomon from seeing the tears in her eyes. "Some of it just has to be good," she said to herself.

When they had salvaged what seed they could, Eliza estimated that it would not plant more than half an acre of indigo. She sighed deeply and said to Solomon, "Well, we will have to make do with this next season."

From what her father had told her about indigo, Eliza knew that she could not hope to make the blue dye until she could raise a large quantity of indigo plants, for many plants would, when processed, yield only a few tiny cubes of blue indigo dye. She ran over what she knew of the process in her mind, eager for the day when she would have enough plants to try to produce the dye. Sometime she would succeed, she comforted herself, but Eliza knew the frost had ruined her last chance for 1740.

And then, after months of silence, Eliza received a letter from her father. He had been so excited over her earlier letter that he had engaged an experienced indigo maker from the island of Montserrat to come to Wappoo to make dye from her next crop of indigo. The man had demanded high wages but would be worth it. Eliza could not believe her eyes. Her head reeled—chills ran up and down her spine. Oh, why had she ever written her father of that promising crop before it matured!

Eliza thought grimly of the first crop that she had planted in March, which a late frost had killed on April Fool's Day; of her second planting in April, which had been virtually destroyed by worms; and then of the third crop she had planted in late May and of the way her hopes had risen when the weedy plants matured and the seed began to ripen, only to have the September frost strike it.

Eliza was nearly sick with frustration. If she had only been able to dry more of the seeds after the last frost struck—then she might produce a good crop for this dyemaker from Montserrat.

It was days before Eliza could get over the shock of the news that her father was sending an indigo maker. Her mother asked her what was the matter with her, but she wouldn't tell.

One Sunday Eliza went to church, as usual, but in a rebellious mood. Out of the sermon she heard only one thought—it was about not borrowing tomorrow's trouble.

That afternoon she went for a long walk in the woods. She argued back and forth with herself. Finally she burst out laughing and said out loud, "I am a goose. I must stop this nonsense now. I will face the indigo issue when I have to. The planting cannot be made until early next spring. Time enough then to concentrate on its nurture. The indigo maker probably will not come until later—somehow it will all work out." She was smiling when she returned to the house.

Feeling the need for diversion and a new scene, Eliza went in early November for a stay in Charles Town with the Millingtons. They had no children and always loved to have Eliza visit them.

Just a few days earlier, a British merchantman, after eluding Spanish ships at sea, had reached Charles Town and filled Mr. Millington's warehouse with goods. On the morning of November 18, 1740, Eliza completed her purchases of warm clothing and blankets for the plantation hands, as well as of all the objects she had neglected to buy during the difficult months just passed.

Then, reverting to a long dormant enthusiasm for beautiful clothes, Eliza purchased yards of a lovely dove-gray glossy silk that would become her mother's pale beauty. She decided her mother needed a new dress for the occasions when she was able to receive company.

After this final morning of shopping, Eliza thoroughly enjoyed the peaceful atmosphere of three o'clock dinner at the Millington home. She had just finished a dish of syllabub for dessert when she noticed a very strong acrid smell in the air. Should she pretend she had observed nothing or should she mention it to the Millingtons? She was slow in answering a question her hostess posed.

Mr. Millington noticed Eliza's slight hesitation and thought it was because it was stuffy in the room. He went to the window and threw up the sash.

"That bitter smell—it's smoke," Mr. Millington declared. "I heard earlier that there was a fire somewhere. He leaned out of the window and pulled his head in sputtering, and gagging. As soon as he could speak again, he said, "I fear the conflagration has worsened."

Just then they heard the sound of running feet in the street. Over the clump of shoes and boots could now be heard the voice of a man shouting, "Fire, fire, fire—to your duty, householders, fire. Fire down to Broad Street."

Mr. Millington pulled out a large cambric handkerchief and mopped his brow. "Ah, dreadful, 'tis what I've long feared," he declared in an ominous tone. "Those tarmakers have let their fires get out of control. My dear wife, I must change to an old suit."

For such a portly man, Mr. Millington made a very rapid change of apparel. When he reappeared, he found Mrs. Millington and Eliza wrapped in their wool cloaks with hoods over their heads.

"What is the meaning of this?" Mr. Millington asked gruffly. "A fire is no place for ladies. This may involve danger and injury to the men who fight it."

"Exactly," declared Mrs. Millington in a very firm voice. "So, Eliza and I have fetched clean linen sheets to take with us. We can tear them into bandages and use them for the men who are sure to be hurt and need nursing. If the gentlemen of Charles Town can fight fires, their ladies can surely nurse them, if needed."

Mr. Millington looked at his wife in amazement. "On those grounds I cannot forbid you," he spluttered. "But neither of you ladies will step out of this house unless you promise to keep well back out of the way of the Fire Masters."

Mrs. Millington bowed her head meekly. "Of course, my dear," she said in her sweetest voice.

People were now pouring down the street. Flames shooting up against the sky left no doubt of the location of the fire.

Mr. Millington kept muttering in his indignation that this fire had been allowed to happen. "I and many others warned about that making of naval stores within the city," he said gloomily.

Eliza chimed in, "Sir, I so well recall your telling my father of the danger the very first day we were in Charles Town."

"By Beelzebub, we'll have a devilish time stopping the flames with that wind blowing in gusts!" Mr. Millington fumed. "Now, remember, you two ladies will gather with other women to the rear and seek only to aid those who are actually overcome in the fire fighting."

He turned to one of his servants who had accompanied them and said, "Plutarch, stay right by the side of your mistress. Do not lose sight of her or of Miss Eliza."

Reaching Broad Street, the party saw Mr. Millington's gloomy prediction already being fulfilled. The wind was fanning the fire. Sparks had spread to wooden buildings. They were old and dry and went up like tinder. Others caught. Homes on the west side of Church Street were now ablaze. Eliza recognized men whom she had met at various social gatherings among the fire fighters. The militia had been turned out. Eliza heard that Colonel Pinckney was on duty farther down the street. Side by side with lawyers and merchants worked the small number of skilled artisans then resident in Charles Town. Landing parties from three of His Majesty's ships of war lying in the harbor and merchant sailors were among the fire fighters, as were indentured white servants, numbers of Negro house servants, and a handful of Indians who had evidently been in town to trade their furs.

In the crowd Mrs. Millington soon located the wife of the chief Fire Master, and together the two organized other women spectators to care for the injured. Eliza worked side by side with her hostess.

There were not only fire fighters to care for but also the families driven out of destroyed homes. Eliza took upon herself the gathering together of children who had become separated from their mothers. Twice she had to dash among the fire fighters to rescue a small boy who insisted on trying to locate his father, whom he feared dead.

The wall of a three-story building flamed like a magnificent torch and then pitched forward in one solid mass, sending the fire fighters scurrying back to safety. One man, however, stumbled over some wreckage and gave himself a nasty fall. Mrs. Millington sent Plutarch and two lads out to drag him to their nursing stand. The man groaned in agony. Several of the women, accustomed to doctoring on plantations, said promptly, "That leg is broken. Someone will have to find Dr. Lining."

The wind seemed malicious in its intensity, and as the fire spread down Church Street, Mrs. Millington and her cohorts realized they would have to move their assistance station. As Eliza helped an aged woman to hobble along, she saw a group of young men with whom she had danced at the Pinckneys' dash by. One yelled, "Turn at the next corner. It's faster that way to the Powder Magazine."

The man with the broken leg was being carried on an improvised litter by Plutarch and two boys. He said faintly, "They are going after powder to blow up houses. 'Tis the only way they will halt these flames. I knew they would be forced to do it."

Before long, they heard terrific blasts as several buildings on Tradd Street were blown up. Some boys who had stolen away from the assistance station came running back to report that the blasting was thought to have halted the fire.

It had been a long and dreadful battle, but the worst was now over, and soon an exhausted Mr. Millington showed up in search of his wife. Others of the men began to filter back from the fire fighting. Plans to house the homeless were made. There was hardly a home standing in Charles Town that did not shelter some unfortunate victim of the fire that night. Few people slept much due to the smoke that hung over the city and the anguish of those who had lost family or homes, or both.

The troopers of the Charles Town Horse Guards patrolled the town to prevent looting.

With the rising of the sun the next day, however, men immediately began to talk of the rebuilding that would have to be done.

Eliza's heart was heavy with grief for the sufferers, but in it glowed a new pride. She had been under fire with these people and seen their staunch courage. She was proud to be one of them. To her it seemed as if she had truly become a South Carolinian through this baptism of fire.

The most immediate need was to replace Charles Town's burned food supplies. Eliza ordered generous supplies to be sent to the stricken city from the Garden Hill and Waccamaw plantations. She herself shipped in as much food as could possibly be spared from Wappoo.

Two collections of money were taken up at St. Andrew's to aid those made homeless by the fire, and similar collections were widely made. Eliza rejoiced greatly when, in December, Charles Pinckney and his fellow members of the Commons House of Assembly passed a bill to restrain the greed of workmen and dealers in building materials. The act set forth just how Charles Town was to be rebuilt and also fixed prices and rates of wages to be effective for the next ten years.

It was estimated that the fire had destroyed nearly three-fourths of Charles Town. No matter how many collections the Carolinians took up for the sufferers, it could not be enough for restoration. Eliza was therefore profoundly grateful when the British Parliament voted £20,000 relief money for Charles Town.

Meanwhile, the people of Charles Town resolutely set themselves to rebuild the burned-out area. Brick was more expensive than wood, but they built of brick to reduce the chance of another such devastating fire. It would take longer to build brick structures, but it was worth it, they felt. Their determination was a challenge to Eliza as she prepared to plant the indigo seeds and try to raise a crop before the indigo maker arrived—the high-salaried man her father was sending from Montserrat. She, too, needed hope and determination to face the future. She had not lost her dream, but she had come to know how hard it was to win the battle with indigo.

Ten

It was a magic morning in late March, 1741. The air was soft with spring's gentleness and fragrant with the scent of yellow jessamine. Warm sunlight shafted through the tall trees to turn the woods of Wappoo into a sylvan cathedral. High in the trees, the feathered choristers sang with total abandon. This heady combination made Eliza feel lighthearted as she and Polly moved through the woods picking blue-purple wild violets for their mother's room.

"Look how much bigger my bunch is than yours, Eliza," Polly chortled gleefully.

"So it is, pet," Eliza declared. "I do believe we have enough. Here, put my bunch with yours."

"Oh, I hope the violets will please Mama," Polly said. "She is so unhappy over not hearing from Papa."

No letters had come from Major Lucas since early January. It was natural that Mrs. Lucas was anxious to hear from him in Antigua, but the Spanish were making it exceedingly difficult for any ships to get through from the British West Indies to the American colonies.

Eliza was as eager as her mother to hear that all was well with her father, but, in addition, she was anxious to learn when Major Lucas was sending the indigo maker.

Well, no matter, the thing to do was to get on with the job that had to be done. That afternoon Eliza ordered the rice planting to be started the next day. The shallow trenches for the seed, about eleven inches deep, were as straight as arrows. With the rice seed in the ground, Eliza turned to her great interest—indigo.

Two weeks later, early in April, Eliza once more watched carefully as the little black seeds were entrusted to the earth. As she had thought when she had salvaged them from the damaged crop the preceding summer, the seeds were only enough to plant half an acre.

"Well, Solomon, we will just have to tend this planting so carefully that it will produce extraordinarily fine plants," Eliza said to her trusted foreman, whom Mr. Deveaux called "head driver of the hoe hands." Eliza's words sounded more hopeful than she felt, but she remembered a favorite maxim of her father's—"Only a fool knows no fear; only a coward runs from the battle."

Resolutely, Eliza kept cheerful before others, but when alone, she had many a struggle in continuing to face her heavy responsibilities. She thought nostalgically of her carefree good times in Antigua with her girlhood friends, Pamela Dunbar and Nellie Brambly, and wished they would write more often. She still missed Rob Leicester, although she had come to believe that she and he had not been intended to marry. Eliza's thoughts often crossed the sea to her brothers in London, where Tommy was not well and George was studying with an army career in mind. Hungry for news of England, Eliza, on May 2, sat down to write George. She urged him to give her "an account of public News, anything that passes worth Notice." George had just turned sixteen, and Eliza told him of her mother's delight at having a letter from Mrs. Boddicott praising his behavior in England.

Shortly before, Eliza had made a new friend—Mary Bartlett, who had come from England to Charles Town to visit her aunt, Mrs. Charles Pinckney. Since Eliza did not wish to leave Wappoo in the busy planting season, she enjoyed writing to this charming girl, who was approximately her own age. Mary Bartlett sent letters back by the patroon. She urged Eliza to come into town to accompany her to social events there. When Eliza recounted to Mary the excitement she had felt at seeing "the comet Sir I. [Isaac] Newton foretold should appear in 1741," Mary wrote back to tease Eliza about her serious interest but asked to know what the comet looked like.

The teasing bothered Eliza not at all, for she thought Mary rather silly to have missed such a beautiful sight. Eliza wrote Mary:

By your inquiry after the Comet I find your curiosity has not been strong enough to raise you out of your bed so much before yr. usual time as mine has been; but to answer your queries. The comet had the appearance of a very large Star with a tail, and to my sight about 5 or 6 foot long; its real magnitude must be then prodigious; the tail was much paler than the comet itself, not unlike the milky way; 'twas about a fortnight ago that I saw it. . . .

The light of the Comet to my unphilosophical Eyes seems to be natural and all its own; how much it may really borrow from the sun, I am not astronomer enough to tell.

May was nearing its end when Colonel Pinckney came out to call. Seeing him stride up the path from the dock on the creek, Eliza ran to the front door to meet him. She greeted Colonel Pinckney with her usual warm courtesy, but the question in her eyes did not escape his attention.

"No, Miss Eliza, I did not bring Mary Bartlett with me," he answered without delay. "I came straight from my office to fetch news of the war to your mother and you. May I see her?"

"Indeed, yes. Mama feels quite well today and is at the desk in the library. She is penning a letter to Papa," declared Eliza with obvious pleasure.

" 'Tis splendid that she is better," Colonel Pinckney said. "But before you tell your mother of my arrival, permit me to turn over these books to you."

With that, he handed Eliza a parcel, which she promptly untied.

"*Virgil's Georgics.*" She read the title aloud.

"I think you will like the *Georgics* because they are all about the joy of country life," Colonel Pinckney declared. "I have brought you the first two volumes—on tilling the land and growing trees. This is a good translation of the original Latin text."

At that moment Mrs. Lucas came to the door of the parlor. "Oh, Colonel Pinckney, it *is* indeed you. I thought I heard your voice. This is a delightful surprise," Mrs. Lucas declared. Then turning to Eliza she added, "Have Cully bring some Madeira for Colonel Pinckney and tea for us."

Eliza hastened to do her mother's bidding and, on rejoining them, was pleased to find Colonel Pinckney still delivering news of his wife and her charming niece, Mary Bartlett.

Eliza had no sooner seated herself than Colonel Pinckney said, "And now, ladies, let me tell you the heartening news that caused me to come for this impromptu visit."

Mrs. Lucas leaned forward eagerly. "Pray, Colonel Pinckney," she urged, "do not keep us in further suspense if the news is good."

"I will delay no longer," Colonel Pinckney said. "A small sloop made port this morning from New Providence Island in the Bahamas. The master of the sloop reported a message has reached New Providence that Admiral Vernon and his attacking force have captured Cartagena from the Spanish."

Eliza could scarcely suppress a loud hurrah!

"What glorious news, Colonel Pinckney," Mrs. Lucas said enthusiastically.

"Mind you, my dear madam, this is not official news, but the shipmaster had sufficient information to make us feel in Charles Town that Vernon has by now reduced that proud city of New Spain," Colonel Pinckney declared.

"Oh, pray that it be so. It might mark the beginning of the end of our war with Spain," said Mrs. Lucas. Her voice was stronger than Eliza had heard it in months.

"We must not be too sanguine, but such a victory could change the course of the war," Charles Pinckney stated. "I know that your dearest hope is for Major Lucas to be able to rejoin you here."

Eliza had listened carefully. "Colonel Pinckney, will we not soon receive some official word if this great victory has been won by our forces?" she asked.

"That is our hope," Colonel Pinckney answered. "The shipmaster reported that on March 23 our British troops reduced the northern fort covering the channel by which ships approach Cartagena. The next day Admiral Vernon sent a dispatch to England predicting the early fall of that port city."

"Surely the admiral would not have sent such a dispatch had he not been sure of victory," Mrs. Lucas remarked.

"That is the considered opinion in Charles Town, so far as I learned it before coming out here," Colonel Pinckney said cheerfully. "The shipmaster told us that there are some 15,-000 sailors and 12,000 soldiers under the command of Admiral Vernon and Brigadier General Wentworth. Even the strong defenses of Cartagena must have yielded by now to a siege by such an armada."

Eliza's thoughts flashed back to Rob Leicester. How he would have loved to have been part of such a force!

She heard her mother say, "If only ships could bring us news more quickly, Colonel Pinckney."

"Yes, the waiting vexes the spirit. Tell me, madam, have you recently had letters from Major Lucas?"

Tears sprang to Mrs. Lucas's eyes, and her mouth trembled. Seeing that her mother could not reply, Eliza said, " 'Tis near six months, Colonel Pinckney, since we have had the pleasure of a line from dear Papa."

But that situation was fortunately soon relieved.

Four days after Colonel Pinckney's visit, Mr. Millington's patroon brought a message to Wappoo. It was a hastily written note, but it said:

A fast schooner has just anchored in Charles Town. The captain tells me that he yesterday overtook Captain Magnus Watson's *Brother's Endeavor*. He learned Watson has had a tedious passage from Antigua. The captain estimates Watson's slower craft will make port tomorrow. Should you care to be on hand for Watson's arrival, doubtless he will bring news and cargo from your father.

"Should I care to be on hand!" Eliza exclaimed as she dashed for her mother's room to read the note to Mrs. Lucas.

Eliza ordered Jethro to be ready early in the morning to take her into Charles Town. She spent that afternoon superintending another weeding of her half acre of indigo.

Tense with eagerness, Eliza was at the dock the next morning to meet Magnus Watson when he landed. She greeted him swiftly and asked, "Oh, Captain, do you have any word of my papa?"

"Aye, that I do, young lady. Here's some letters for you

and your ma. I have a cargo Major Lucas sent you—rum, the finest and driest Muscavado sugar, molasses, and one to two thousand weight of coffee. Your pa ordered the cargo was to be sold and allowed that you and Mr. Millington knew what to do with the proceeds."

Eliza could hardly wait to read one letter from her father that was addressed to her, but she managed to say, "Oh, thank you, Captain Watson; yes, we know my father's wishes."

"One more thing, Mistress Eliza. The major said for you to fill my hold as fast as could be, as I aim to be off rapid-like. I got through safe coming up, but 'twas a slow passage. So, I must hasten to return."

"I will have the plantation boats loaded at once to fetch the stuff to you," Eliza replied. "I have shingles and lumber to go, salt meat, two barrels of rough rice, two of corn, three of peas, and a keg of eggs I have preserved in salt to see if they can be used in Antigua."

"I'm powerful glad you've got the cargo ready for my return. Your pa sent a passenger by me, too," said Captain Watson. "He was so busy staring at Charles Town when we anchored that he didn't have his gear ready to come ashore with me."

Eliza's eyes widened in surprise. "You mean you've brought the indigo maker on this trip?" she asked breathlessly.

"You guessed right, young lady. I think that's him now," Captain Watson declared as he pointed a stubby finger at a figure in the small boat making a second trip to the dock from the *Brother's Endeavor*.

Eliza's mind was a battleground of conflicting emotions. She was intensely excited that the indigo maker had actually arrived, yet fearful of what he would think of her small field of indigo plants.

She watched intently as the man climbed out of the small boat onto the dock and reached down for a canvas bag of belongings a sailor handed up to him.

The man was small of stature, quick and nervous in his motions. As he turned and faced her, Eliza felt an instinctive distrust of him. His swarthy face was heavily pitted from smallpox. His small, bright beady eyes stared boldly at her.

"Mistress Eliza, this is Nicholas Cromwell," Captain Watson said. "I picked him up at Montserrat according to your pa's orders. He's an indigo maker, but I reckon your pa's told you to expect him."

Forcing herself to ignore her foreboding, Eliza gave Cromwell a courteous welcome.

He barely answered before asking, "When do I see this indigo your father says you've raised?"

"As fast as the patroon and his men can row us to the plantation."

When they reached Wappoo and Eliza showed Cromwell her small stand of leggy indigo bushes, Cromwell's face revealed his disgust. "Not enough plants here," he said, "to bring me all this way."

From the first Nicholas Cromwell was gloomy about the prospects of indigo in South Carolina. He was forever bragging about the island of Montserrat and saying how it was naturally suited to the growing of fine indigo.

Trying to keep from arousing Cromwell's temper was a new experience for Eliza. She had been surrounded all her life by courteous people—her family and friends, their Negro people, or the mannerly English servants at her school in London.

Efforts that Eliza made to encourage Cromwell only seemed to make him more negative than ever. But his unrelenting pessimism about the possibility of growing indigo and producing a good dye in Carolina only spurred Eliza on. She had a deep-seated faith in what she was trying to achieve, a belief that indigo would be produced in this British colony. And she was determined to do it!

To Eliza's surprise, Nicholas Cromwell demanded brick with which to build vats for the dyemaking process. She looked at him to see if he were joking.

"Mr. Cromwell," Eliza replied to his request, "I have not been able to lay hands on a book about dyemaking, but I did come across one on grape culture and the fermenting of grapes. I have heard the process with indigo is not entirely different. For turning grapes into wine, they use wooden vats."

Cromwell glowered in his resentment at this girl's daring to make suggestions to him. He finally controlled himself enough to speak. "Mistress Lucas, I am the indigo dye specialist sent here by your father. I request brick with which to build the vats." Cromwell snapped out the words.

Eliza longed to rebuke him for his rudeness. On the tip of her tongue was the reply, "You may be an expert, but you are engaged to work for me and to be polite about it." But she bit her lip and fought back her anger. Finally she said quietly, "I shall order the brick from Charles Town. It will take extra time to get it. The wood we have here on the place."

Eliza could not shake off her feeling that it was wrong to use brick vats. Like her father, the girl had "hunches," or presentiments, and this was one of them, so much so that she rode over to Westpenny to consult her old friend, Mr. Deveaux.

Mr. Deveaux considered her query for some minutes before replying. Then he stated in a calm, controlled way, "I regret the man's manner toward you, but he has an element of truth when he says he is the expert sent to teach you. So, since your father believed in the man's skill and has gone to vast expense to send him here, 'tis only sensible to allow him to do it his way. I always say, 'Never consult a doctor and refuse to take the purging he orders.'"

Mr. Deveaux rubbed a long thin finger up and down the side of his aquiline nose as he waited to see how Eliza would take his little homily of advice.

She smiled gently and said, "Yes, I suppose it is all I can do, even though I strongly feel it will be harmful in the end."

Eliza sent to Charles Town for brick. There was no brick yard with piles of ready-made brick sitting around in great stacks, and as a result there was a considerable wait for them to be fired and delivered.

Eleven

Finally the two long bateaux of bricks arrived, and Nicholas Cromwell set about building his vats. During the wait for the materials, Eliza had suggested to him that he dig the foundations, but he had replied he did not build that way. So, now, with the bricks piled all around him, Cromwell had the slaves belatedly digging trenches for the foundations. His procrastinations annoyed Eliza, but she kept silent.

One rule on the Lucas plantation was that orders were to be obeyed, but equally emphasized was an insistence that orders be clearly expressed and not given in a spirit of either abuse or temper. Major Lucas had stressed this often to his daughter, pointing out that it was a rule of command he practiced in the army as well as with the slaves whose lives he controlled.

It was, therefore, very upsetting to Eliza when she heard the consistently bad-tempered way in which Cromwell gave orders to the Negroes assigned to work under him in building the brick vats.

On the first day of the construction work, Eliza ignored Cromwell's harsh rudeness to the workers. She tried to persuade herself that he acted this way because he was nervous about starting a new job in a strange country. After two more days of it, however, she saw him kick a Negro who had misunderstood an order. She felt obliged to rebuke him and to request that he treat the men decently.

Nicholas Cromwell gave her a hard stare and then spat to one side. "I gotta drive them," he declared beligerently, to get a lick o' work out of them. They are lazy savages from the jungles of Africa and won't work."

Eliza felt a cold fury seize her. Truly this man was worse than she had thought. "They have worked extremely well for us," she said with as much control as she could muster. "I shall tolerate no abusive treatment of them."

The indigo maker narrowed his eyes, looked as if he were going to reply, then clamped his mouth shut and turned aside.

After that rebuke from her, Cromwell seemed to delay deliberately over the brickwork. She tried to show she bore no ill feeling, but the man from Montserrat retained his sullen manner.

Eliza decided that the best thing she could do would be to avoid watching Cromwell do his work as much as possible. Maybe he resented her being a girl; maybe it made him nervous to be watched. In any event, she would keep her problem from her father, who already had enough to worry about.

So, she sat down at the desk in the small library and wrote to Major Lucas far away in the Caribbean area. She thought it only fair to warn him that there would be little of value produced from the indigo this year, but then reaffirmed her belief.

I make no doubt Indigo will prove a very valuable commodity in time if we could have the seeds from the East Indies in time enough to plant the latter end of March that the seed might be dry enough to gather before our frost.

Eliza's quill pen moved on and on.

The death of my Grandmama in Antigua was, as you imagine, very shocking and grievous to my Mama, but I hope the consideration of the miseries that attend so advanced an age will help time to wear it off. I am very much obliged to you for the present you were so good to send me of the fifty pound bill of Exchange wch. I duly received. We hear Carthagene is taken.

Eliza had given the French spelling to Spain's chief South American port that had been attacked by Admiral Vernon.

Unfortunately, the news of the certain victory proved false. It was a bitter blow to Eliza, as well as to all loyal subjects in the colony, when the news reached South Carolina that the British expedition against Cartagena had been defeated. Gradually reports of the disastrous affair came through in detail.

Eliza felt her heart constrict when she read in the paper that Wentworth had delayed so long that when he had ordered the attack in force, the British had met with a bloody repulse. Reading on, she learned that yellow fever had devastated the British force. All too clearly she realized that what had happened to these fighting men could happen to her father. Her heart felt like a stone. Would peace never come?

Nicholas Cromwell had dallied so long in completing the brick vats that the leaves of many of Eliza's indigo plants yellowed and withered off. Uncertain as she was about the rest of the dyemaking process, Eliza *did* know that the quality of the dye was dependent on the fresh, unbruised state of the leaves.

At last the vats were done, and Cromwell agreed for the indigo to be cut early the next morning and brought in from the field.

Eliza was in a fever of excitement when the work began. She tried to hide it, determined not to show her eager interest to Cromwell for fear it would antagonize him again. She prayed silently that they could produce even a little dye. It would so encourage her father in faraway Antigua. She knew how Major Lucas must need cheering after the recent defeat of British arms.

Eliza stayed out in the field to see that the men cut the indigo plants carefully and that the leaves were not bruised. The bluish tinge of the leaves had to be retained as they carried them to Mr. Cromwell. Then she took up an unobtrusive position on the far side of the brick vat from the dyemaker. She watched how carefully the indigo plants were laid in the vats with the stalks up and how clear the water was that covered them.

Of a naturally friendly and kindly disposition, Eliza soon forgot the surly manner of Cromwell. She was lost in excitement that the time had finally come to see if her plants would produce the valuable blue dye.

When the vat was filled and the steeping process began, Eliza's face was radiant with enthusiasm. "Oh, Mr. Cromwell," she said impetuously, "we are so fortunate to have a dyemaker like you who knows all the secrets of the trade."

Nicholas Cromwell's thin face clouded over with bitterness, and he muttered to himself, "Yes, I am selling my birthright. I'll probably ruin my own island by coming here and teaching the process. My mother was right about it. I should not have come."

His words cut Eliza like a lash. She took one last look at the vat on which so much depended and walked swiftly toward the house. This process of actually turning the plants into dye was something Eliza had dreamed of for nearly two years. She had worked hard to grow the plants and had looked forward to this as a time of great joy. Instead, Nicholas Cromwell seemed determined to ruin it for her. Eliza was convinced that he should have used wood instead of brick for the vats and that he had deliberately dawdled at building them. What did he have to fear from so small a beginning? It would take years to establish a real indigo business in Carolina, Eliza reasoned. Besides, Cromwell was being paid highly, and her father had engaged him with the specific agreement that she was to watch every step of the process.

The process of indigo making was one that required time and great care. For some twelve hours, the indigo plants, with their leaves on them, had to ferment under water in the vat called "the steeper." During this time the chemical *indican,* which existed mainly in the leaves, dissolved in the water. Bacteria and enzymes transformed the *indican* into *indoxyl.* The decomposition that was taking place made the liquid foam. Then the solution was drawn into a lower vat called "the battery," where it was vigorously beaten with paddles for several hours. The paddling carried on the foaming fermentation and exposed a maximum amount of the solution to the air, which converted the *indoxyl* to *indigo.* During the latter part of the beating, the indigo maker took frequent samples. The minute he perceived a purplish blue tinge in the solution, he had to decide the amount of limewater to add, which, stirred in gently, would stop all fermentation and precipitate the "bluing."

When this bluing substance had settled at the bottom of the battery, the fluid was drawn off and the blue paste scooped up and strained through a sieve into linen bags. These were drained and then kneaded to press out as much remaining moisture as possible. The substance left was cut into cubes and placed out of the sun to dry slowly at as even a temperature of air as was possible.

The main steps of the process that lay ahead were known by Eliza from what her father had seen on Montserrat and told her. She did not, however, know the chemistry of the process nor the proportion of limewater to be added to precipitate the blue dye.

In the house at Wappoo, when she had had time to recover somewhat from the bitter remark Nicholas Cromwell had made, Eliza decided she simply must return to the scene of the indigo making. Too much was at stake, and she did not know what Cromwell might do. Eliza decided she had better take Polly with her. At least she would have a member of the family by her side. Their mother was ill in bed with a rather severe attack of malarial fever.

Polly was full of curiosity about the dyemaking. In spite of the bad smell of the fermenting indigo plants, Polly peered into the steeping vat, which was about sixteen feet square by about two and a half feet deep. Excitedly, Polly asked question after question.

Mr. Cromwell watched this in disgust and gave Eliza a look that clearly said, "This is no place for children or childish interest." But Eliza had made up her mind not to be thrown off balance by Cromwell's antagonism. She watched very carefully as he drew off the liquid from the steeping vat into the "battery" built close by on a lower level. Because of the small number of plants and Cromwell's delay with the vats, which had diminished the number of usable plants still further, there was not a large amount of the liquid. Cromwell then growled to the slaves working under him to get their paddles. He inspected each paddle to see that it was clean and ordered the men to start beating the liquid, fortifying his orders with a string of coarse words.

Cromwell muttered at the men, "You lazy rascals. Beat harder, I tell you."

Eliza edged nearer. "Mr. Cromwell," she asked, "do you do that to expose as much of the liquid as possible to the air?"

Eliza's recollection of what her father had told her was correct, but Cromwell only replied coldly, " 'Tis the system. Can't explain it to you. It takes long to learn the method."

Eliza knew that Cromwell would never have made such a reply to a man. She sighed. It was so hard to be a girl and have men treat her as a dunce. Her present situation was also difficult because it was bad for her people to see this employee flaunt her authority on the plantation.

Eliza decided that Cromwell's treatment of her might well cause trouble and that she had best go and discuss it with her dear and faithful friend, Mr. Deveaux. Daylight would hold for her to go and return.

The elderly gentleman listened calmly to her account of the man's rudeness. "He is taking advantage of the fact that you cannot produce the dye without him," he said, "and, therefore, he thinks he can do as he wishes. I believe I had best ride back with you and observe Cromwell at work. I will fetch a lantern for my return here. 'Tis conceivable Cromwell might work harm to the indigo if he dares speak to you like that."

So, Mr. Deveaux stood close to Eliza and little Polly at the high moment of the process when Cromwell was to add limewater to the much-paddled mixture. Eliza was plagued by a thousand doubts.

She kept her concern to herself until she saw Nicholas Cromwell walk away and turn his back on them to measure the limewater. It was hard to see him even though lanterns and pitch-pine torches had been placed around the area. Eliza gently tugged at Mr. Deveaux's sleeve and whispered, "How much is he going to put in?"

The Huguenot's usually serene face was very stern. He clucked his lips in irritation at Cromwell and walked in a circle around the man until he could see how much limewater he was measuring out. Instantly, Nicholas Cromwell leaped up from his crouching position, seized the buckets, moved toward the brick "battery," and emptied the limewater into the mixture.

Once more the dyemaker ordered his helpers to get their paddles and showed them how to stir the limewater into the juice.

"Now, Mr. Deveaux," Eliza murmured, "I will just have to pretend that I have a little patience, which I do not feel, and wait till the lime has worked its process on the juice. Then we will learn how many solid grains sink to the bottom of the vat. Oh, I find it hard to wait!"

"I'm sure you do, my child, you have worked so hard for this moment. And it has been a long time coming."

Walking slowly over to Nicholas Cromwell, Mr. Deveaux said, in a quiet, courteous tone, "Tell me, Mr. Cromwell, about what are the proportions of limewater usually administered to the juice?"

"A dyemaker must have that knowledge within himself," Cromwell replied. "I'm tellin' you if anything goes wrong, 'tis the poor quality of the plants themselves. Dammit, this climate ain't suitable to indigo. I'm a man that knows his trade, and I ain't cheerful about this mess of stuff I'm handling now."

Eliza noticed that Cromwell did not dare speak to a man as he had to her, but his manner was still resentful and surly.

The wait, of course, seemed interminable to the eager girl. Mr. Deveaux, having decided he must remain at Wappoo, was resting at the house. She herself stayed near the vat almost constantly. She wished to make sure that neither Cromwell nor anyone else had a chance to play a trick at this stage. Eliza knew that dust thrown into the vat could ruin everything.

When Cromwell actually pulled the bung and started to drain off the fluid, Eliza dispatched a runner to the house to bring Mr. Deveaux back to see the final results.

As soon as all the liquid had drained away, a thick scum of soft blue paste could be seen on the bottom of the vat. Cromwell scraped this out, put it in linen bags, let the liquid trickle out, and shaped the remains into little cubes. He carefully laid the cubes on clean wood trays that had been made earlier. The Negroes set them under a shed so that for the next days the dye could dry slowly without being cooked by the sun.

Eliza stood staring down at the small cubes. Her heart was pounding, and she felt as if she could hardly breathe.

Mr. Deveaux chuckled. "Mistress Eliza," he said, "would that I could paint your face at this very moment, tired as I know you are. In your eyes there is a mixture of rapture and amazed humility. I must tell you that I rejoice with you. This is a great moment not only for you but for everyone in this colony and for the Crown of England as well. Soon England will not have to rely on French Pondicherry or Martinique, Montserrat, or the Spanish for the commodity. Those few blue cubes prove that indigo dye can be made in South Carolina. Some have raised the plant here, my child, but I have not heard of anyone producing the dye before. It may have been done, but I believe the honor of being the first to achieve it is yours. Mademoiselle, mes salutations." Mr. Deveaux lapsed into his native French as emotion mounted within him. He graciously added, "Now you give us all courage to try."

The elderly man bowed very gravely to the eighteen-year-old girl.

Her eyes brimming with tears of joy, Eliza curtsied to Mr. Deveaux in appreciation of his tribute.

As she rose from the curtsy, she caught Nicholas Cromwell's muttering, "An inferior grade. On Montserrat, I'd be ashamed of such dye."

But not even Cromwell could dampen Eliza's happiness. She was not ashamed, for she felt sure that in the future they could improve the grade. Her dreams had come true, at least partly true. Now, she could write her father that they really could produce the much-wanted blue indigo dye on Wappoo plantation. It would make money. Perhaps now they could pay off the mortgage!

Mr. Millington was one of the first people Eliza wanted to tell that indigo had been made at Wappoo. She sent him a note but explained that Cromwell declared the indigo to be an inferior grade. To the Charles Town merchant, Eliza confided her belief that the indigo maker had deliberately failed to make the best dye possible.

Just after the cubes of indigo had fully dried, Mr. Millington showed up at Wappoo plantation. He was accompanied by a black-haired man with a great beak of a nose and piercing eyes.

"Miss Lucas," Mr. Millington said, "may I present Captain Duclos, who brought a cargo of wheat flour from Philadelphia into Charles Town harbor yesterday. The captain is French by birth. While we were enjoying a rum punch together last night, I learned that he used to sail into Martinique to buy indigo and transport it to France. I asked him to come out to see your indigo and judge its quality."

"How thoughtful of you, Mr. Millington, and how very good of you to do this, Captain Duclos," Eliza said with warmth in her voice. She turned aside and called to Cully, "Go fetch Mr. Cromwell to the indigo shed at once."

They went immediately to the drying shed. Captain Duclos picked up cube after cube of the indigo and studied each one carefully. His face grew somber.

"Where is your indigo maker, Mistress Lucas?" Captain Duclos asked suddenly. "I must speak to him."

"I have sent for him," Eliza replied.

Just as she spoke, Nicholas Cromwell ambled slowly into the shed. He tried to look nonchalant, but Eliza noticed that his hands were shaking.

Captain Duclos stared at Cromwell. In English that bore a heavy French accent, the sea captain demanded, "Do you call yourself an indigo maker?"

Cromwell's face went crimson, and he answered belligerently, "I am one of the best on Montserrat."

"Then why did you ruin the color of this indigo by putting too much limewater into the solution?"

The color drained out of Cromwell's face. He made no answer.

"Why, I asked you?" Captain Duclos repeated angrily. As he advanced toward Cromwell, he looked as though he were about to hit the indigo maker, who was visibly terrified.

Cromwell backed off. "Don't strike me. Don't. I could not make fine dye here. I feared 'twould ruin the trade for Montserrat."

Mr. Millington's face showed his amazement. He said, "So your suspicions were correct, Miss Eliza. Cromwell deliberately made an inferior grade of indigo. Next time you will produce only the finest. Meanwhile, you should be very proud; you have succeeded in producing indigo in South Carolina."

Twelve

Eliza's indigo success gave her a new assurance—what had been achieved on a small scale could be improved and widely carried out. Achievement proved both a comfort and a spur.

She found it easier to face all the old problems that were still hers—the continuance of the war with Spain and her father's absence; the long waits between letters from him; her fear of his being wounded or killed in battle; Mrs. Lucas's failure to recover robust health; the unending daily decisions about management of the plantations and care of the slaves; Polly's preference for play over schooling and her need for friends of her own age; the unceasing battle with nature—whether it was too much rain or too little, worms or insects in a crop, unexpected frost or protracted spells of heat.

She wondered, too, about her own future. Was it to be, as she wrote a cousin, that "I should never get a man to answer my plan and must therefore die an old maid?"

Her joys deepened now as well. Eliza looked forward each morning to that first view of the sun as it rose in the east to dispel the mists that hung over Wappoo Creek and then turned all things new for the day. Each evening she thrilled at the pulsing beauty of the western sky as it turned gold, orange, red before the earth once more accepted the mantle of darkness. The fun of the children in the quarters; the joy over a new baby born there in the sick house; the friskiness of her mare and the gentleness of Polly's pony; the loyalty of an old dog who followed her wherever she went—all gave her pleasure.

Life was fascinating to Eliza. Her days were full but never too full for one more dream, one more project. For her, it was not enough to produce indigo, even though no other colonist had been able to do so. She fell to thinking of the years ahead when ships would be built in South Carolina. That would require great timbers and fine planking! Trees would take time to grow, she reasoned. And so Eliza set out a large planting of oak trees to be available for ship timbers "when oaks are more valuable than they are now, which you know they will be," as she wrote to her friend, Mary Bartlett. She wrote also that two-thirds of the profits from the oaks were to be given to charity.

Eliza knew that Mary read all her letters to Colonel and Mrs. Pinckney, and this pleased her. It amused Eliza that Charles Pinckney jokingly called her "the little visionary." It was not a title Eliza minded a bit, and she instructed Mary to tell Colonel Pinckney that "what he may now think whims and projects may turn out well by and by—out of many surely one may hit."

One of the projects that Eliza hoped might hit the bull's eye of success was a planting of fig trees. To Mary Bartlett she wrote:

O! I had like to forget the last thing I have done a great while. I have planted a large fig orchard, with design to dry and export them. I have reckoned my expense and the profits to arise from those figs, but was I to tell you how great an Estate I am to make this way, and how 'tis to be laid out you would think me far gone in romance, Yr. good Uncle I know has long thought I have a fertile brain at scheming, I only confirm him in his opinion. . . .

But all was not planning and planting for Eliza. In late October, 1741, the patroon, Jethro, returned from a trip into Charles Town bearing a box that had come from London. It had crossed the Atlantic in one of the ships that would carry rice back to England under protection of a convoy to protect them from the Spanish.

To Eliza's enchanted delight, the box contained materials for new dresses for herself and her mother—a present ordered by Major Lucas in far-off Antigua.

Mrs. Lucas laughed gaily. "Eliza, you do love fine clothes as much as I, and that color does so become you," she declared.

Polly was upset because there was no dress material in the box for her. "There, there, my darling, some of this fine cambric your father has sent shall be used to make you some lovely new night-rails. I will have them trimmed with lace."

Polly's face lost some of its pout, but she still didn't say anything.

"I shall bring you something pretty from Charles Town when I go tomorrow," Eliza announced.

With that promise, Polly capitulated.

The next morning Eliza went into town for a visit to Mrs. John Cleland, a very dear friend of Mrs. Pinckney's. Mrs. Cleland, an heiress to lands in South Carolina, always invited Eliza to the parties she and her husband gave. This time the celebration was in honor of the King's birthday, an event annually observed in Charles Town, both publicly and privately.

When Eliza saw Colonel Pinckney, she had many questions to ask him, for he had lent her some books by his favorite English philosopher, John Locke. Earlier, when Carolina had been under the control of The Lords Proprietors, John

Locke had written a model constitution for the colony, but this had never been put into effect. Colonel Pinckney, however, often quoted Locke's theories of government and praised his essays pleading for broader religious freedom.

As usual, Eliza managed to mix the frivolous with the serious, and on her return to Wappoo she not only brought Polly a pretty warm muff but also some materials to make herself some lappets. It was the height of fashion for ladies to do elaborate embroidered pieces, called lappets, to wear in the puffs of their high-piled hair. Because of her father's disapproval of embroidery, Eliza had not before attempted the intricate work necessary to make them.

Before long Mary Bartlett sent a note out from Charles Town to inquire how Eliza was progressing with the lappets. Eliza wrote her back a schedule of her work week and concluded:

Now you may form some judgement of what time I can have to work my lappets. I own I never go to them with a quite easy conscience as I know my father has an aversion to my employing my time in that poring work, but they are begun, and must be finished. I hate to undertake anything and not go thro' with it, but by way of relaxation from the other, I have begun a piece of work of a quicker sort wch. requires neither eyes nor genius . . .

There was no question that Eliza loved to dress up, look pretty, and to charm the opposite sex. But neither was there any doubt—that she was determined not to marry until she found the man both heart and head told her was right for her.

When Major Lucas wrote her proposing that she marry a wealthy older man "Mr. L.," who had asked him for her hand, Eliza wrote back to her father that "the riches of Chile and Peru put together, if he had them, could not purchase a sufficient Esteem for him to make him my husband."

She continued:

As to the other gentleman you mention, Mr. W., you know, Sir, I have so slight a knowledge of him I can form no judgement, and a Case of such consequence requires the nicest distinction of humours and Sentiments.

But give me leave to assure you, my dear Sir, that a single life is my only Choice;—and, if it were not, as I am yet but Eighteen, hope you will put aside the thoughts of my marrying yet these two or three years at least.

Well did Eliza know her father's love for her. She was confident that, unlike the fathers of some girls of her acquaintance, he would never force on her an arranged marriage, no matter how wealthy the man who asked for her hand.

Early in the year 1742, Eliza received a letter from her father in reply to her report to him of Nicholas Cromwell's treachery.

Major Lucas was as angry as Eliza that Cromwell had acted disloyally but explained that he could not dismiss the Montserrat man from their employ because he had signed a long-term contract with him. As wrong as Cromwell's actions had been, Major Lucas did not feel that those acts released him from his contractual agreement with the indigo maker. So, he advised Eliza to send Cromwell to work under Overseer Murray at their Garden Hill plantation.

Major Lucas concluded his letter of advice:

Murray is absolutely loyal and will be able to see that Cromwell works. But, do not again have Cromwell make indigo—at either plantation. I will look about here in the islands for another indigo maker. The ship's captain who hired Nicholas Cromwell for me has now admitted that he has always been a trouble maker. The captain says Cromwell's younger brother Patrick is honest and a good indigo maker. Perhaps, eventually, I can engage him to come to South Carolina to make indigo for you. I will look into the possibility.

Eliza was delighted to send Nicholas Cromwell away from Wappoo. She wished she could send him back to Montserrat, but she agreed with her father—they had to keep their part of the contract even if Cromwell had failed to lived up to his. She realized also that Cromwell might work well under Murray since he was not to be required to make indigo.

She decided that she would not that year attempt to make the dye at Wappoo but would grow as large a crop of indigo as she could and save the seeds to plant the following year. Perhaps by that time her father would send her Patrick Cromwell, or some other reliable indigo maker, and she could then make really good dye.

All of Eliza's plantation worries were forgotten when happy news reached Wappoo plantation in February, 1742. Major George Lucas had been promoted to lieutenant colonel. What was more important, his long service on His Majesty's Council in Antigua had caused him, on December 12, 1741, to be appointed Lieutenant Governor of that island. He would be second in responsibility to William Mathew, the Royal Governor of the Leeward Islands, but would also continue his military duties. Lieutenant Governor Lucas warned his family that it would take a long time to secure regular pay from the Crown for his extra services. Meanwhile, the Assembly of Antigua would reward him with presents.

"The pay is not the important thing," Mrs. Lucas declared. "I so rejoice that my dear husband's ability has received this recognition."

Eliza was as proud as could be but could not help wondering whether this would put an end to the hope of her father's exchanging his military post in Antigua for a similar one in Georgia or South Carolina.

On June 30, 1742, there was great alarm in Charles Town when an express courier arrived from Georgia with news. A force of twelve hundred Spaniards had landed near Fort Frederica on St. Simon's Island, Georgia. Not only that, but General Oglethorpe had heard that the Spanish were preparing an even more formidable expedition to recapture the coast as far north as Port Royal and maybe even attack Charles Town.

The whole of Charles Town was aroused to a fever pitch of preparation. British men-of-war in Charles Town harbor were sent to the Georgia coast immediately. Meanwhile, as Charles Town soon learned, General Oglethorpe repulsed the Spanish by a defeat at Bloody Marsh, Georgia, on July 7 and in subsequent fighting.

The Spanish commander, sighting the two ships that had been sent from Charles Town, believed they were a part of Vernon's fleet and retreated. Captain Hardy tried to pursue the Spanish ships, but bad weather forced his return to Charles Town.

It was soon learned that the Spanish were regrouping to attack the Georgia and South Carolina settlements. Palisades were driven all around the lower end of the peninsula on which Charles Town was located. This would prevent the landing of any enemy troops, it was thought.

Only when this protective measure was taken did Mrs.

Lucas give way to Eliza's pleading to enter Polly at Mrs. Hicks's boarding school in Charles Town. The number of girls there delighted gregarious Polly.

A few weeks later the girls at the school and everyone in Charles Town rejoiced when a part of His Majesty's Jamaica fleet sailed into the harbor to protect South Carolina. There were seven transports with over five hundred of Brigadier General Wentworth's soldiers on board. More exciting were the accompanying British men-of-war, H. M. S. *Shoreham* and H. M. S. *Spy,* commanded by Captain Broderick.

Mr. and Mrs. Cleland promptly sent a note asking Eliza to come to town to stay with them. The first officer Eliza met there was Captain Broderick. Since he was an old friend of her father's, he was delighted to see Eliza.

The Spaniards made no coastal attack, and the contingent of the Jamaica fleet, sent to protect South Carolina, still rode in the harbor when the King's birthday dawned on Saturday, October 30, 1742.

That afternoon every lady in Charles Town was keyed up like a taut violin string as last-minute preparations were made for the ball that evening.

When Eliza entered the ballroom, she let out a little exclamation of delight. The jewels worn by the ladies and the dress swords, epaulets, and shiny buttons of the officers caught the light from the hundreds of candles in the overhead chandeliers. The whole room was aglitter. Eliza thoroughly enjoyed the ball and wrote her father afterwards of the attention she had received.

There was much gaiety in Charles Town during the stay of the Jamaica fleet. Anticipation ran high when the announcement was made that another ball would be held. Eliza, who loved to dance, was as disappointed as anyone when it was learned that the *Shoreham* was to sail on November 3 and also the *Hawk*. The Spanish threat had shifted to the West Indies, and so the land forces were to be returned to Jamaica with these ships as convoy.

Mrs. Cleland was appalled when she heard the news. Captain Broderick, who was calling at the Cleland home, noticed her agitation. "Lest the Spanish scent weakness here," he said, "it is arranged that His Majesty's ship, the *Spy,* is to protect Charles Town, as well as the *Rye,* which will come in from her searching cruise."

"The plans seem most carefully drawn," murmured Eliza.

Captain Broderick nodded agreement and added, "Captain Joseph Haymar is also to bring in the *Ross* and *Flamborough* in a few days."

Thirteen

"Eliza, your father is at last not only a lieutenant colonel by rank but also lieutenant colonel of his regiment," Mrs. Lucas exclaimed happily as she looked up from a letter she had just receieved.

"Has Lieutenant Colonel Valentine Morris resigned from the 38th Foot?" asked Eliza.

"No. I am sad to say he has died, but he had been in very poor health for some time. Your father says his regimental promotion is definite, and his commission will be issued in London certainly by early April. Oh, there's more—your father will continue as Lieutenant Governor of Antigua while also carrying out his army duties," Mrs. Lucas declared proudly.

The window in Mrs. Lucas's room was open to let in the warmth of the March day in 1743. Sunlight illuminated her face, and Eliza thought she had seldom seen her mother look so happy. She herself was delighted.

"Do read on, Mother. Does Papa say anything of brother George?"

"Yes," Mrs. Lucas replied. "He writes that George has been a joy to him ever since he arrived from England and began his duties as an ensign in the regiment."

"Oh, how I'd love to see them both, and Tommy, too. He

must be ever so lonesome at school in London without George," Eliza commented.

The good news from her father gave Eliza a new spurt of energy. She enlarged her class of Negro children and took special satisfaction in teaching them to read and write. Eliza discovered that they learned more now that Polly, with her teasing ways, was no longer a fellow student. Polly, too, was happier at the boarding school in town.

Polly's absence also left more time for Eliza to pursue her own education. She had become sufficiently skilled in music to have a more advanced teacher—Carl Theodorus Pachelbel, the organist of St. Philip's Church in Charles Town and son of the distinguished German composer and organist, Johann Pachelbel. Under his tutelage Eliza deepened her appreciation of fine music and increased her proficiency on the harpsichord. She continued to work faithfully at improving her French, but her exciting new interest was law. She was studying a law book by a Dr. Wood but found it much harder to understand alone than when Colonel Pinckney explained it to her. Eliza reported on her new interest to her confidante, Mary Bartlett, still a house guest at Belmont:

Nor shall I grudge a little pains and application, if that will make me useful to any of my poor Neighbors. We have some in this neighborhood who never think of making a will 'till they come upon a sick bed, and find it too Expensive to send to town for a Lawyer.

If you will not laugh too immoderately at me, I'll trust you with a Secret. I have made two wills already! I know I have done no harm for I con'd my lesson very perfect. . . . But after all, what can I do if a poor Creature lies a-dying and their family takes it into their head that I can serve them. I can't refuse; but when they are well and able to employ a Lawyer, I always shall [refuse]. . . .

Her many activities and plantation supervision could not long keep Eliza's thoughts from her father. The lack of any letter from him throughout the spring and early summer of 1743 filled her with foreboding. Finally this long silence was broken. As Eliza had feared, the news from Lieutenant Colonel Lucas was not good. He reported his participation in an elaborate naval and military expedition that had been carried out against Spain's chief seaport in Venezuela.

The objective of this British expedition had been to capture La Guaira and nearby Puerto Cabello. The 38th Foot, of which Robert Dalzell was the commanding colonel and George Lucas the lieutenant colonel, had taken a major role in the attack. The regiment had, unfortunately, been short some men.

When the attack had actually been made, on April 16, 1743, Lieutenant Colonel Lucas had been in command of the landing party. It had consisted of men of his own regiment, all the marines of the squadron, and four hundred seamen from the warships. There had, unfortunately, been delay before this landing had been attempted, and the Spaniards had prepared fully for the attack. As Lieutenant Colonel Lucas had led his troops against the Punta Brava batteries, the Spaniards had poured forth a withering fire. Men had dropped by the score. The other Britishers had broken ranks and fled in complete disorder. George Lucas had gone among his men ordering and then pleading with them to halt their rout, reform their ranks, and charge the enemy. His efforts had all proved in vain. Smarting over this distressing failure, Lieutenant Colonel Lucas and his fellow officers had returned with the troops to Antigua. From there he had written this long account to his wife and daughter.

Heartsick over this military defeat, George Lucas was more eager than ever to be reunited with his family. He wrote that he longed to bring them back to Antigua since he was unable to leave his joint duties as regimental lieutenant colonel and Lieutenant Governor. Lucas declared that he would try to get leave for his son George and send him to escort Mrs. Lucas, Eliza, and Polly back to the West Indies. Tommy, who had been ill in London, should also come home so they could all be together again.

Eliza, who had so often complained of how long it took a ship to bring mail from Antigua, now comforted herself that her brother George might also take a long time to come for them. Much as she wanted her family to be together, Eliza realized how attached she had become to South Carolina. And she had so hoped to make really top-grade indigo dye in another year. Oh, if only George could wait a year and her father would send to her the indigo maker Patrick Cromwell!

In the fields at Wappoo and at the Garden Hill plantation, Eliza left a large crop of indigo standing until sun and air should dry the seeds. There would be enough seed to plant a great deal of indigo the next season. In her eagerness to bring off a final glorious indigo success, Eliza consoled herself with the thought that maybe Mr. Deveaux would see it through for her after she left for Antigua.

When Colonel Charles Pinckney heard that Eliza would soon have to leave South Carolina, he proposed a tour of farewell visits. Mrs. Pinckney was not well, and she thought this series of country visits might do her good. She said Eliza's company would be a tonic in itself. Soon the three set out together by carriage to visit various friends.

The highlight of the trip for Eliza was a week's visit to the William Middletons at Crowfield. The garden was very beautiful, and there, Eliza wrote a friend, she listened to "a variety of airy choristers pour forth their melody, and my darling, the mocking bird, joined in the artless concert and enchanted me with his harmony." The unaccustomed leisure of this visit also gave Eliza time to read Samuel Richardson's romantic novel *Pamela,* about which everyone was talking.

The country tour was a happy experience but did not prove as beneficial to Mrs. Pinckney's health as had been hoped. That fall illness forced her to bed. Eliza sent delicacies and notes to her friend and went to Belmont to call whenever she could.

Meanwhile, there was news of another illness. Young Ensign George Lucas had contracted a severe case of smallpox in Antigua. The physician could not advise how long it would be before he could leave for South Carolina.

On a December visit to Mrs. Pinckney, Eliza realized for the first time that her friend might never recover. She tried to cover up her dismay by regaling Mrs. Pinckney with an account of Charles Town's preparations to receive James Glen. He had been appointed Royal Governor of South Carolina back in December of 1738 but was only now, in December, 1743, coming to reside in Carolina. Eliza had gone out to Belmont from town, where she had been staying with Mr. and Mrs. Cleland. She had deliberately delayed her Christmas shopping so that she could be in the city for the Royal Governor's arrival.

On December 19, when the British man-of-war *Tartar* reached the harbor with Governor Glen, Eliza was on the wharf with Mrs. Cleland and a group of the most distinguished ladies of the province. The cannons boomed out a welcome to the Royal Governor. His Excellency came ashore and was greeted by Charles Pinckney and Edward Aitkin of His Majesty's Council. Eliza was proud to note that Charles Pinckney exhibited his usual charm and graciousness of manner to Governor Glen, even though his heart was heavy over the critical illness of his wife. Like any other twenty-year-old girl, Eliza enjoyed the glittering pomp and ceremony of the occasion.

A more personally exciting arrival for Eliza was that of her brother George, who landed not long afterwards from Antigua. He was still thin and pale from his long illness, his face scarred with pocks from the smallpox, but the sight of him gave Mrs. Lucas renewed strength. She was even able to cope with the news from England that young Tommy's health had not improved.

Mrs. Pinckney continued to fail. Worn out from her long illness, she died in January of 1744. Her death was a great grief to Eliza and to her mother. They attended the funeral, accompanied by young George. Mrs. Pinckney had been much beloved, and nearly everyone of note in South Carolina came to her funeral, including Royal Governor Glen. It seemed sad to all to think of the much-esteemed Charles Pinckney being bereft of his wife before he was even forty-five.

Lieutenant Governor Lucas had sent young George to South Carolina in the belief that a British man-of-war would soon be available to transport his family back to Antigua. Official needs, however, kept the warships busy elsewhere. When Lucas learned this, he decided to go ahead with his earlier plan and sent Patrick Cromwell by a merchant brig to be the indigo maker at Wappoo.

The arrival of this more promising brother of the deceitful Nicholas Cromwell caused Eliza's hope to soar once again. Maybe she would still have a chance to make one wholly satisfactory batch of indigo dye before she had to leave South

Carolina! If she could do this, Eliza felt sure that Carolinians would carry on indigo production after she was gone. This dream of Eliza's, however, was discouraged by her brother. George insisted that a British man-of-war would become available by late spring to transport them to Antigua.

Fourteen

Preparations now began in the Lucas household for the return to Antigua. As much as Eliza longed for all her family to be together again, she had quite lost her heart to this new country. She felt that, like her indigo plants, she too, had become accustomed to the soil of Carolina. She said nothing to her mother or her brother, who were enthusiastically packing up for the move, but she felt a deep ache inside.

The neighbors gave entertainments to welcome George Lucas, Jr. The parties were designed also as preliminary farewells to the family they had become so fond of. Eliza endeavored to enter into the gaiety, but she was frank in admitting to her friends how much she would miss them and Carolina.

One wintry day, when the overcast sky made a grayness that fitted her mood, Eliza gazed pensively out of a parlor window. She was absent-mindedly staring at the familiar view of winding Wappoo Creek and nearby Sandy Island. The harsh cawing of gulls flying overhead was as melancholy as her thoughts. Would she always have to move on, meeting new people and making friends but never finding the one person in whom she could lose herself and build a fully satisfying life? Was that joy to elude her always?

Suddenly a movement on the creek caught Eliza's attention. It was a pettiauger heading for the Wappoo landing.

She could not imagine who might be arriving. Jethro was not in town, and they were not expecting anyone.

Eliza decided she might as well go out to the landing to greet the guest. Restless and sad as she was, she would feel better for a taste of the winter air. She threw a mantle about her and walked swiftly to the edge of the bluff to discover who the visitor could be. To Eliza's surprise and pleasure, she saw it was Charles Pinckney. His handsome face lit up at the sight of her. "Ah, Mistress Eliza, you are a sight to cheer one on this gray, wintry day," he said.

Colonel Pinckney asked Eliza about her mare, which had been ill with colic, and what further news she had had from her father. He was courteous, as always, but he seemed to have his mind on something else. For the first time since she had known Charles Pinckney, Eliza felt constraint between them. To her surprise, he asked immediately if he could see Mrs. Lucas and George. There was an underlying note of seriousness in his voice that puzzled her. But Eliza replied, "Why, certainly. Mama has just finished her nap, and I will send for George, who is at the stable seeing about my mare."

When Mrs. Lucas and George reached the parlor, Eliza took a seat near her brother, for she did not dream that Colonel Pinckney had meant he wished to see her mother and George alone. She watched Charles Pinckney lean toward her mother and murmur something. Shortly afterwards, Mrs. Lucas said, "Eliza, I wish you to go down to the sick house and see how Essie feels since the birth of her child. Bella has been muttering about her, and I feel nervous about the girl."

Eliza's always large eyes opened even wider. What in the world was the matter with her mother? She had visited Essie only an hour ago. Why was Colonel Pinckney acting so strangely? Suddenly she realized that *he* had suggested her leaving. It hurt her sharply, for, if anything, Charles Pinckney was a special friend to *her* rather than just a family friend.

But her mother, for all that she was frail, knew how to indicate by her voice when she wanted something done and done right away. Eliza left the room immediately. She flung her mantle on and headed for the women's section of the sick house. Ezra's wife Essie, who was full of vitality, was already in high spirits. With her happy-go-lucky ways, Essie was one person who paid no attention to Bella and her airs of importance. Eliza was sure that that was the only reason Bella had muttered about the younger woman. When Eliza sat down now beside the new mother, Essie was full of boasting that hers was the handsomest baby born at Wappoo since they had come from Antigua. Essie and her baby were the only inhabitants of the sick house, and Otelia was there to look out for them. Eliza soon wandered over to the childen's house.

Ordinarily Eliza loved watching the Negro children make up games that copied grown-up life. Today they were playing house, using wood chips for plates and acorns for make-believe food. One young boy had exactly copied Cully's stiff-legged walk and pretended he was the butler serving the meal. Today Eliza was miserable and could not enter into the game. She felt as if her dearest friend had just slapped her. Had she offended Colonel Pinckney in some way? What could he wish to discuss that he would not say before her? The room of happy children suddenly became unbearable. She went to the door and unlatched it to leave.

But someone was opening it from outside. The door swung open, and there stood Charles Pinckney.

She remained gazing up at him stupidly, for his face now looked entirely different. It had lost the somber expression of an hour back. He seemed elated and energetic.

"Mistress Eliza," he said in his warm, deep voice, "will you come with me at once?"

He seemed to be hurrying her down "the street" of the quarters. He said nothing but kept his head turned toward her. The minute they were out of hearing of the last cabin, he said, "I cannot wait longer to ask you, Miss Eliza. I want you to marry me and stay always by my side. I cannot have you leave South Carolina. This return to Antigua is, of course, right and proper for your mother and Polly, but not for you. You have brought something into my life and to all of us who know you here that cannot be spared."

The two had reached an arbor built of cedar, and Charles Pinckney steered Eliza into it. He stood close. "I will cherish you as no other man could," he said very quietly but with great intensity. "I had not realized how utterly dear to me you have become until I heard that George was seeking passage to take you and the family back to Antigua."

Eliza's heart was pounding as if it would burst her ribs. Her head felt as if it were floating off and she was in a dream. What was Charles Pinckney saying to her? Had she heard correctly?

She placed her hand on his arm to steady herself and continued to gaze up at him. She, who could usually find words for every subject, was speechless—that her beloved Charles Pinckney should wish to marry her was beyond any dream she had ever entertained.

He leaned down and took her two small hands in his. "Oh, my dear little one, you are startled. 'Tis sudden, but circumstances force me to act with haste. George just confirmed to me the rumor I had heard that he is trying to secure passage very shortly. I would have preferred to have paid court to you and wooed you less precipitately. I simply could not risk delay, for I must have your father's approval back here before George leaves."

Eliza finally found her tongue. "I am almost breathless," she said so softly that he had to lean closer to hear her. "But 'tis not because you are acting with such speed but because it seems nothing short of a miracle that you wish to marry me."

"Your mama has given her approval and also George. My dear little Eliza, please say my proposal pleases you," Charles Pinckney said earnestly.

When they repaired to the parlor in the house, the two found it discreetly empty. They talked on and on.

Charles Pinckney came almost daily now to press his suit for Eliza's hand. She put up many arguments, for she felt genuinely unworthy of the man she had so long admired and looked up to.

A letter had gone promptly to Antigua to Eliza's father, but when a reply could be expected was entirely uncertain, owing to the war with Spain and the fact that now France had come into the struggle. It was all a part of the general European War of the Austrian Succession.

Nonetheless, Charles Pinckney felt assured that Lieutenant Governor Lucas would grant his approval since Mrs. Lucas had already done so, as well as George. What he was more interested in now was winning Eliza's heart. It was not easy for him to come out from Charles Town, for his law practice was heavy and now that he was a member of His Majesty's Council, as well as of the Commons House of Assembly, he had many meetings to attend. Governor Glen was pushing forward new plans for the colony.

This very fact, the high position that Charles Pinckney occupied, was one thing that made Eliza hesitate. One day she burst out, "I am but just approaching my twenty-first birthday. I am not at all certain the eminent people of the colony will think me a suitable wife for you."

Charles Pinckney threw back his head in his hearty laugh and then took her hand gently in his. "My dear little friend," he said, "allow me to judge of your gifts. You possess what I deem the richest possession there is, the power to enjoy, and this is one of the things about you that so refreshes and charms me. I love your questing mind. You can be entrancingly gay or winsomely serious. My friends are greatly pleased with you. Why, you are a veritable favorite of all. I think you are teasing me."

Eliza was deeply moved by what he said of her. A sudden moisture had sprung into her eyes, and she tried to hide it. She turned her head.

Charles Pinckney leaned over and gently turned her head back. "There is so much more I could say," he murmured. "Your enthusiastic admiration for the achievement of others delights me. I like that kind of generosity. My part in governing the colony and planning for its future is not easy, but your support would cheer me in it. In my official life ahead, there will always be the necessity of meeting new people and trying to turn strangers into friends. You are so charming in the way you treat the meeting of a stranger as a gay adventure. You cannot believe how that ability of yours would help me. And also, I like your loyalty and devotion to old friends and those dependent on you. Believe me, Miss Eliza, you have truly captured my heart, and that is what I offer you."

Eliza gave a little sob of delight. That was what she had been longing to hear, that he loved her for her very own self. She leaned toward Charles Pinckney, who was seated at the other end of the parlor sofa. "No other marriage could ever make me so happy," she murmured very softly. "I love you very tenderly and very deeply, and I admire you with all my heart and mind."

Now that she had let herself go, Eliza discovered how deeply she cared for Charles Pinckney. At last she realized why she had never loved Rob Leicester or any of the other young South Carolinians who had showed her attention. She had measured them by Charles Pinckney, the man who seemed to her to possess every desirable attribute. How she reveled in his sparkling conversation! She loved to see his mobile face light up with kindness and understanding. She marveled at his naturally modest manner, though he held such distinguished posts of leadership. Her dream had come true—she had found a man "to answer her plan."

Even though she considered herself engaged and only waiting for approval from her father to set the wedding date, Eliza did not overlook the planting of her 1744 crop of indigo. On April 1, she was out in the field to make sure that the little black seeds were sown just right. The ground had been prepared in January, and furrows were now made. Eliza was taking no chances on this crop. She intended it both for dye and seed to parcel out among various planters so that the crop might be really established in South Carolina. Mr. Deveaux was again raising a field of indigo, and Eliza had her overseer, Murray, planting a large acreage in it at their Garden Hill plantation on the Combahee River.

Eliza did not mind being busy. It would shorten the time until they could hear from her father—whether he refused or granted her permission to marry Charles Pinckney. At last the letter came. Lieutenant Governor Lucas was very pleased over the match. He offered the most generous settlement he could. In pursuance of the custom of the time, he wrote that he much wished he could give the Wappoo plantation as Eliza's dowry, but this was not possible because of the mortgage he had earlier placed on it. However, he did make a small financial settlement, and he and Mrs. Lucas gave to Colonel Pinckney the indigo then growing at Wappoo. Eliza was distressed that she had not yet perfected her indigo culture to the point where profits from it could have lifted the mortgage. It did please her, though, that at least her experimenting and work had provided a main item of her marriage portion.

Since most brides in her station of life brought their husbands handsome fortunes, Eliza was much touched when Charles Pinckney declared to Mrs. Lucas, "No settlement whatever is necessary. I am marrying Mistress Eliza for herself. I am happy with any arrangements whatever that Governor Lucas has made but would be content if he had made none."

Now the usual flurry began over a trousseau for the bride-to-be. Eliza refused to have an extravagant wardrobe because of the expense of moving the family back to Antigua that was about to fall on her father. She and her mother did make a number of trips into Charles Town, however, to the mantuamaker and milliner. There were also slippers to be secured to match each gown. Eliza ordered extra high heels; she had always wished to be taller than she was.

Eliza was radiant in her new happiness. It was going to be hard to have her family so far away, but as an army officer's daughter, she had long ago resigned herself to separations. She knew she would miss her parents and Polly and her brothers dreadfully, but Charles Pinckney would make up for all of them. A thing that disturbed her more was the possibility that her dear Charles might be criticized for marrying so soon after losing his first wife. Mrs. Cleland quickly reassured Eliza on this point. "Naturally, my dear," she said, "there has been some discussion of it. But many of us know how Mrs. Pinckney esteemed you, and we who were her friends believe she would thoroughly approve of this marriage. As to its taking place so soon, everyone understands that that is a necessity caused by your family's departure."

Fifteen

Eliza Lucas and Charles Pinckney were married quietly on May 27, 1744, with her rector, the Reverend William Guy, performing the ceremony. It was the kind of day that all brides dream of for their wedding. Eliza's friends, "the airy choristers," perched outside on bough and bush, were ecstatic in their warbling. The young bride was equally ecstatic with happiness.

So that Eliza should not be separated any sooner than necessary from her mother, Charles and Eliza decided to stay on at Wappoo plantation until the Lucases sailed for Antigua. They were waiting to secure passage in a merchant ship as Lieutenant Governor Lucas had been unable to arrange for his family to travel by warship.

Finally, after the long wait, everything suddenly happened at once. Charles Pinckney's mother, Mrs. Mary Pinckney Betson, fell dangerously ill, and he had to go to Charles Town to attend her. Then Samuel Millington, Governor Lucas's agent, withdrew from business because his wife had received a very large legacy. At this juncture, accommodations in a merchant brig were obtained for the Lucases and their house servants. In a wild flurry, Eliza completed the last-minute packing for her mother. The July night before the Lucases sailed, the bride wrote her father that Charles Pinckney would be glad to handle for him the business that

Mr. Millington had managed. Because of all the recent excitements in the family, she added, she would have to defer sending her plantation accounts.

After seeing her family off to Antigua, Eliza had a busy two days closing the house at Wappoo and setting out work for the slaves that remained. Charles Pinckney then carried his bride off to his own home, the handsome Belmont plantation, five miles from Charles Town on the Neck.

There Eliza spent a summer of great happiness, thoroughly enjoying the fascinating companionship of her husband who, she wrote, "has never left me but one day in the week since I have been here."

Together they planted trees—magnolias, oaks, mulberry, and any foreign species they could lay their hands on.

Though she had moved from Wappoo, Eliza kept in constant touch with the plantation and the progress of her indigo crop. This year she believed her efforts would be crowned with real success. Patrick Cromwell was more cooperative than his surly brother, seeming eager to make up for his brother's disloyalty. Eliza consulted Charles Pinckney now about all she did. He took over some of the business but wisely did not cut off his young wife's initiative.

Finally Eliza's 1744 crop was harvested. From her planting at Wappoo, some seventeen pounds of very good dye were manufactured by Patrick Cromwell, while a quantity of seed was saved. Her old neighbor Mr. Deveaux had also made some dye from his planting. All the plants at Garden Hill were allowed to go to seed. These Charles Pinckney, with Eliza's full approval, gave to other planters to start indigo crops the following year.

No further proof was needed that a fine grade of indigo could be produced in South Carolina. The government of the colony promptly offered a bounty of "five shillings currency" for each pound of indigo dye to be produced there. Charles Pinckney took six pounds of the dye produced at Wappoo and sent it by a British man-of-war to England to show the government that the commodity they so desired could now be produced in Carolina. With that sample went the request for a bounty from the Parliament of England.

On a pleasantly warm afternoon in early October, Eliza and Charles Pinckney were seated on the piazza of their house at Belmont. Eliza looked with admiration at her youthful-looking husband. His dark hair was cut very, very close to his head. When at home without guests, the dignified member of the Royal Council loved to cast off the wig he had to wear when pleading a legal case, and in cold weather he would wear a jaunty velvet cap, though only in the heart of the family. Eliza resolved that a portrait of him must be painted.

Charles Pinckney's thoughts, however, were on matters of larger importance. "Eliza," he said, "the war in which England is engaged may prove to be the very thing that will make the British Parliament grant a bounty on South Carolina indigo."

"Why would that be so?" Eliza asked.

"This is my reasoning. France made a great mistake when she sent those powerful squadrons to the West Indies to support the Spanish. Before that, the war was only a fight about who should sit on the throne of Austria, but that move turned it into a general war and brought Italy in on the Spanish side. And now the French have turned loose hordes of privateers to attack British merchant ships. So, the indigo dye that England needs for her big weaving industry cannot be secured from either Spain or France. England must look to us for the dye, and Parliament will grant South Carolina a bounty to encourage the large-scale production of indigo here."

"Splendid. Truly splendid, my dear. But how soon will England start paying that bounty to us?" Eliza inquired.

"Ah, dear wife, you will have to be patient. Parliament moves slowly," Charles Pinckney declared with a wry smile.

Eliza frowned. "I hate more waiting. It has taken four long years to achieve success with indigo."

"Yes, my little love, and you have showed more patience than I thought any woman possessed. Without boasting of you publicly, may I tell you once more here in our own home that I am enormously proud of your achievement. I shall do everything possible to see that the making of indigo becomes a major affair in our colony. All planters who have a light, rich soil will soon be growing it, I predict—especially up toward the Winyah section. From indigo great wealth will be made. And your country will owe it largely to you. You persevered when others had given up."

Not long afterwards, Eliza told her husband of her wish to undertake silk culture at Belmont. Charles Pinckney made no objection, although he warned her that it had been a long time since raw silk had been produced in South Carolina at a profit. In late 1744 Eliza had many additional mulberry trees planted at Belmont. This was her first step toward her new project. Next she began reading everything she could find on silk culture. She asked merchants to look into sources from which she could import the eggs of silk worms when she was ready to attempt the production of silk.

One day that November of 1744, Charles Pinckney surprised Eliza. "I believe I should build a handsome house in Charles Town to be a very special setting for you, my lovely wife," he announced. "We will plan it together and design it so that it will suit the entertaining we will do in years to come."

Like any bride, Eliza was greatly pleased at the idea of a brand-new house for their brand-new life together.

By the time the new year of 1745 arrived, Charles Pinckney was all ready to go ahead with the house in Charles Town.

It was to be a "mansion house" built of plum-colored English brick with stone copings. It would be set in the middle of a whole block of property extending from Market to Guignard Street, on the western side of East Bay. There would be plenty of room for Eliza's garden. The house would face the water and have a lovely view. Construction was started almost immediately.

Eliza loved to go into town with her husband to observe the progress of the building, but she was kept very busy with her duties as mistress of Belmont and of her husband's other plantation on the Ashepoo River, Auckland, that Charles had inherited at the death of his father, Thomas Pinckney. Eliza also continued active in the supervision of the three Lucas plantations, although she was wise enough to see that her husband had the final decision in all business matters.

On February 25, 1746, Eliza Lucas Pinckney presented her husband with their first child. They promptly named him Charles Cotesworth Pinckney. Eliza insisted on Charles for the baby's father, and her husband asked if they could add Cotesworth, his mother's maiden name, to avoid confusion with his own.

Even her delight in her first-born child did not keep Eliza from plantation duties and new experiments. She undertook to raise flax and hemp for which Lieutenant Governor Lucas sent her the seed. At this time, Eliza also introduced weaving at the Garden Hill plantation. Her father sent her two Irish indentured servants, one a weaver and one a spinner. Eliza arranged to have Pompey, the carpenter, build a loom. Tackle for it was secured from Charles Town. When Eliza's experiments with flax growing did not produce any great quantity of that fiber, Eliza set the Irish spinner and weaver to work on wool and cotton. She also had the Irish couple train two Negro women to work as spinners. Spinning wheels were made for them, and soon the weavers were producing enough wool cloth to supply the winter needs of the Negroes on the Lucas plantations.

Letters went from Eliza and Charles Pinckney to Lieutenant Governor Lucas detailing plantation affairs. After long waits, they heard from him. He was worried about the drop in the price at which his rice could be sold. He wanted Eliza to continue the experiment with flax. Most of all, he looked for indigo to be the money-maker that would lift his mortgage on Wappoo. To help increase the quantity and quality of the indigo dye, Lieutenant Governor Lucas sent an expert Negro indigo maker from one of the French islands to replace Patrick Cromwell. Patrick had made better dye than his brother Nicholas but not a superior quality and not enough of it. It was the Negro dye maker who was to seal Eliza's success with a truly fine grade of indigo.

With the indigo that Eliza and other planters produced in 1747, South Carolina was able to export 134,000 pounds of indigo dye that year, and the British Parliament then voted the bounty that Charles Pinckney had urged. This made the product so profitable that exporters estimated indigo raisers in South Carolina would be able to double their capital every three years, or every four at the least.

Eliza was at the time expecting her second child. She and

Charles had already decided that if it was a son, he should be named for her father, George Lucas. Eliza was ailing that early fall of 1747, and Charles Pinckney insisted she give up some of her work. He was most solicitous about her health—overly solicitous she came to believe. One day not long before the baby was expected, Eliza decided to bring her plantation accounts up to date. While searching for a paper that she had mislaid, she found a letter addressed to her and Colonel Pinckney from Mrs. Lucas. It had been kept from her! As Eliza read, she soon learned why her husband had hid the letter from her. It was an anguished report of the death of her father!

George Lucas had been captured in 1746 from an Antigua ship by the French. He had been taken to France as a prisoner and had died in Brest in January of 1747. Eliza's beloved father was dead—she would never see him again!

The shock unnerved Eliza as nothing before ever had. She and her father had always been so close. Her grief was compounded by the fact that she had not been told promptly so that she could have written her mother. This preyed on her mind.

Charles Pinckney had been wiser than Eliza knew. Her grief over her father's death precipitated the birth of the baby. As she and Charles had hoped, the infant was a boy and they named him for her father, but little George Lucas Pinckney died in two weeks.

This second loss proved almost more than Eliza could bear. She had looked forward to a reunion with her family when she could proudly show them her sons—especially this child who was to carry on her father's name.

Charles Pinckney knew just how deep the bond had been between daughter and father. He tried to comfort Eliza and rally her spirits. For once, she lacked the will to fight—she could not throw off her grief over the loss of her father and her son. For the first time, she found no joy in living.

Eliza had suffered greatly during George's birth. Now she was very ill. Her recovery was slow, but gradually her strong constitution won the physical battle, and she claimed the victory over grief and depression. When at last she resumed her normal life, she deliberately turned to an experimental interest.

Earlier, she had sent to France for the seed eggs of silkworms. The needed silkworms had been produced in quantity, and the slave children had been taught to feed the leaves of mulberry trees to the worms. Following her recovery from the loss of her baby, Eliza diverted herself by devotion to this silk producing project. She mobilized every housemaid at Belmont and all the elderly women on the plantation to work with her.

The place where the caterpillars, or silkworms, were hatched had to be kept scrupulously clean and disinfected with limewash. Eliza used her well-trained housemaids to do the cleaning, and a man then did the whitewashing. The children would bring in the mulberry leaves and feed them to the caterpillars. It took about forty-two days for the feeding, and the children marveled that the caterpillars could eat about twenty times their own weight in ripe leaves.

When a caterpillar was ready to spin its cocoon, it raised the front part of its body and waved it slowly from side to side, spinning as it moved. When the cocoons were fully spun, the older women began their careful work. First they exposed the cocoon to the sun to dry. Then they boiled the cocoons in water to soften the natural gum holding the filaments together. Finally they reeled the raw silk thread from the cocoons.

It was an intricate process and one that Eliza never tired of teaching to her workers.

On August 8, 1748, Eliza and Charles Pinckney's grief over the loss of their baby George was lessened by the birth of a little girl, whom they named Harriott. The couple still wanted another boy and were delighted when a son was born to them on October 23, 1750. They named him Thomas after Charles' father and now felt their family was complete.

It was a relief to Eliza and Charles Pinckney that great Britain's war with Spain and France was finally over. A general peace treaty had been signed at Aix-la-Chapelle on October 18, 1748. It was, however, impossible for Eliza to forget that peace had not come in time to save her father's life. She never stopped missing her family and wrote often to them in Antigua.

Eliza was as busy as could be, rearing her three children, directing her silk culture and the weavers her father had sent over, and carrying out her duties as mistress of Belmont and her social obligations as wife of the leading lawyer of South Carolina. She even wrote out two "Receipt Books" to help her in planning her entertaining.

In 1752, Charles Pinckney was chosen by Royal Governor Glen to become Chief Justice of South Carolina, the second highest office in the colony. The appointment met with general approval in South Carolina, and to Eliza it seemed a very fitting honor for her brilliant husband. As Chief Justice, Charles Pinckney was the embodiment of the type of official Carolinians wished to direct them. There had long been a great deal of feeling in the colonies that England saved all the top jobs for Englishmen and gave few to men who lived in and knew the colonies. Pinckney's appointment quieted some of this discontent, for the Carolinians fully expected

King George II to confirm him. After Charles Pinckney had worn the robes of office and fulfilled his duties for over half a year, an English gentleman, Peter Leigh, was sent to Charles Town, with the Royal Commission, to take over the Chief Justiceship. Political shifts in England had caused Leigh's removal as High Bailiff of Westminster, and the ministers of the government felt obligated to find a place for their ousted adherent. Since the King had not yet confirmed Pinckney, the ministers persuaded the Crown to give the high South Carolina post to Leigh.

This ruthless replacement of the much-loved and respected Charles Pinckney infuriated the Carolinians. Eliza ached for her husband and for the Carolinians, for it was an insult to the people of that proud land. But, as always, Charles Pinckney counseled moderation and a decent acceptance of the Chief Justice who had the needed royal approval.

Charles Pinckney's fellow citizens were determined not to accept this slight without a murmur. They would show the Crown how much they believed in this man! And so they offered him the position of Commissioner of the Colony in London, where he would handle the business of the Royal Governor of South Carolina, the Council, and the Commons House of Assembly with the Lords of Trade and of Plantations, as well as with other official boards in London. Many people urged Eliza to persuade Charles to accept this semi-ministerial post, even though it carried only a small salary. She thanked them and smilingly said, "The Chief Justice will do what he feels is right." Like other Carolinians, she continued to call Charles Pinckney by that title.

At length Charles Pinckney decided he should represent South Carolina in England. Because his absence would be a long one, he rented their "mansion house" in Charles Town to Royal Governor James Glen.

Sixteen

The Pinckneys set sail in March, 1753, for England and Charles's new post. In addition to all their other luggage, Eliza took with her on the sailing vessel a quantity of the raw silk she had produced at Belmont and some singing birds in a cage. Twenty-five days later, after much seasickness, Eliza, her husband, and three children arrived in England. Smallpox was raging, and so the Pinckneys decided they must risk having the children go through the rather new and uncertain process of innoculation.

Once this was over, Eliza set about having her silk woven into material for gowns: one for the Queen Mother of England as an example of colonial industry, one for the lady of Lord Chesterfield because he had proved himself such a good friend of the American colonies, and one to be a shining gold brocade for herself!

As agent of the royal province of South Carolina, Charles Pinckney was soon received by King George II. Since the King's wife was dead, Eliza felt it fitting for her and little Harriott to pay their respects to the widowed Princess of Wales, mother of the young Prince of Wales who would some day be George III of England. It was decided that Colonel Pinckney would accompany them, as the Princess of Wales was in residence at her summer home at Kew. Harriott was to present to Her Highness the birds they had brought from Carolina.

On their first visit to Kew, however, they arrived late and could only leave the birds and return the next day. And that time they arrived promptly at one o'clock in full dress. They had to wait a few minutes, and then they were escorted by a gentleman of the court through some magnificent chambers to the dressing room of the Princess of Wales. There, as Eliza wrote later:

. . . we were received in a manner that surprised us, for tho' we had heard how good a woman the Princess of Wales was, and how very affable and easy, her behaviour exceeded everything I had heard or could imagine.

She came forward and received us at the door herself, with Princess Augusta, Princess Elizabeth, Prince William and Prince Henry. She met us with all the cheerfulness and pleasure of a friend who was extremely glad to see us; she gave us no time to consider how to introduce ourselves or to be at a loss what to say, for she with an air of benignity, told us as soon as we entered she was very glad to see us, took Harriott by the hand and kissed her, asked her how she liked England, to which she answered, 'not so well as Carolina' at which the Princess laughed a good deal, and said it was very natural for such a little woman as she to love her own Country best. She thanked her for the birds, and said she was afraid one of them might be a favorite of hers; spoke very kindly sometimes to Mr. Pinckney, sometimes to me, and then to the Child.

Apparently the threesome from Carolina, with their unusual gift of a deep-blue indigo bird, a nonpareil finch, and a yellow bird, quite charmed the Princess of Wales, for she dismissed all attendants from the interview. She herself introduced each of the little royal princes and princesses, herself kneeled on the floor to comfort four-and-a-half year old Harriott when the excited child cried, and took her upon her lap. She sent her eldest daughter for the Prince of Wales, who with his brothers asked Charles Pinckney many questions concerning South Carolina.

The Prince also inquired particularly of the Pinckney sons and for what careers they were intended. The future George III was as gracious as his mother.

Eliza and her husband enjoyed five interesting years in England. First they lived in a rented house on Craven Street, London. Then they bought a villa at nearby Ripley. They attended the theater often to see David Garrick, the great actor of the day. They journeyed to the watering resort Bath and visited in the homes of their many English friends. Eliza renewed many schoolgirl friendships, especially one with Lady Nicholas Carew.

The schooling of the three young children was closely supervised by Eliza while Charles Pinckney, as agent for South Carolina, worked constantly for fairer treatment of the American colonies. To this end, he carried on a correspondence with Lord Pitt, the enlightened British statesman who recognized that England should avoid coercion in handling the settlers of the new world across the sea.

Because of the problems caused South Carolina by the French and Indian War and also because of the need to attend to personal business, Charles Pinckney decided he should make a trip to Charles Town in 1758. Eliza and their daughter would accompany him, but it was decided that the boys should be left in London to prepare to enter Westminster School. Eliza found it hard to part from twelve-year-old Charles Cotesworth and eight-year-old Tom but looked forward to a quick return. She little dreamed how long it was to be before she saw them again. Charles, Eliza, and little Harriott sailed for Charles Town. Perhaps because he had been so long away from the Carolina swamps and the mosquitoes that bred there, Charles Pinckney was stricken with a severe attack of malaria shortly after their return. Eliza and his physician thought the fresh sea breezes at nearby Mount Pleasant might assist in his cure and so moved him there. But it was to no avail. Charles Pinckney died on July 13, 1758.

It was a blow that Eliza could scarcely sustain—her strong, vigorous husband torn from her side. Somehow she would have to go on without this man she adored, who, she wrote her mother, had made her "for more than 14 year the happiest mortal upon Earth!" Her grief was deep, so overwhelming that it came near wrecking her health. Finally she reclaimed the valiant courage that had been her outstanding quality.

Eliza was determined that their sons, Charles Cotesworth and Thomas, should still receive the finest education available. And that, to her, meant schooling in England. The words of her husband's will were fixed in her thoughts—each son was to be brought up not only liberally, but virtuously and to make "the glory of God and the good of mankind . . . his principal aim and study." Through letters she would tell them of their father and his great emphasis on the "dignity of human nature." She would have to be both father and mother and influence them through weekly letters since she could not be near them.

Once more, Eliza was busy from morning to night managing the plantations and business properties left by her husband. She continued to rent the mansion house to successive royal governors and lived at Belmont plantation. There she increased her indigo production and other crops. Her holdings were extensive, but money was hard to collect. Education of the boys at the famous Westminster School in London, then Christ Church, Oxford University, and then their law studies in the Middle Temple, London, were enormously expensive. Apparently because of the possibility of war with the mother country, they also studied military science at the Royal Military Academy at Caen, France. Eliza's heart ached over the long separation from her sons, but difficult days had come upon the American colonies, and she was working toward a great aim. Not only must she carry out the wishes of her husband; whatever the cost, her sons must be trained for responsibility in America's future.

Eliza followed with interest the enormous growth of the indigo trade and rejoiced over the wealth it had brought to the colony, especially after Moses Lindo came from London and taught the planters how to sort and grade the dye. She conferred on plants and trees with botanist-physician Dr. Alexander Garden, for whom the gardenia was named. She gave devoted attention to rearing her daughter and was to rejoice when Harriott blossomed into a charming young woman and married Daniel Horry in February, 1768. Letters from Charles Cotesworth and Tom were a source of great happiness to her. The views they expressed were important to her. With them she longed for the Crown to put a stop to tyrannical treatment of the colonies.

When George III failed to speak out, Eliza thought back to the scene at Kew and how this same king, then a boy, had been so gracious to each of them and so interested in Carolina. Surely the man could not be too different from the boy! He would wish to halt the injustices.

But gradually Eliza came to believe, as many leading South Carolinians did, that the King's attitude was inflamed by a tax-hungry Parliament. She understood why her sons, like other American students in England, were signing petitions and actively working to inform the British of the injustices being perpetrated against the colonies. Charles Cotesworth and Thomas went to Parliament to hear the debates and were better informed than most men back in Carolina. So vehement was Tom in his arguments for liberty that he became known at Oxford as "the little Rebel."

No mother stood more proudly behind her sons when they returned to South Carolina and were among the first to volunteer to bear arms in the colonists' War for Independence. It was not easy for Eliza to renounce a lifelong habit of loyalty to the Crown. It had been instilled in her by her father, a British army officer and Lieutenant Governor of Antigua, and nurtured through more than half a century. But others besides her had to face this wrench of loyalties. Like Eliza, they chose to join the signers of the Declaration of Independence and risk their lives, their fortunes, and their sacred honor for the cause they believed right.

Eliza Lucas Pinckney saw her sons rise from junior officers to become the friends of Washington. The two young men suffered through long years of arduous campaigning, capture, and imprisonment and the confiscation of their estates. They knew constant concern for the safety of their wives, Charles Cotesworth having married Sarah Middleton in 1773, and Thomas marrying Elizabeth Motte in 1779.

As Eliza had stood up to Nicholas Cromwell and the defeats of her early years, so now she fearlessly faced the British, who raided and plundered and finally seized Belmont as well as the mansion house in Charles Town. She lived through the horrors of invasion and great personal impoverishment but remained confident that the justice of the American cause would bring it triumph.

After Yorktown signaled the end of the war and independence was finally won, Eliza accepted the urging of her daughter Harriott to come and live with her. Harriott's husband, Daniel Horry, had died, and she wanted her mother with her at Hampton on the South Santee. There, at that great plantation, the woman who had lived through so much once again enjoyed, in peace, the beauties of nature and the gaiety of grandchildren. Sometimes she helped advise Harriott about the plantation, but mostly Eliza devoted herself to rearing Harriott's daughter and the three daughters of Charles Cotesworth Pinckney, who had lost his wife.

A delegate from South Carolina to the Federal Constitutional Convention in Philadelphia in 1787, Charles Cotesworth had a hand in helping to draft the Constitution of the United States. That same year Thomas became Governor of South Carolina. Both brothers played prominent parts in getting the Federal Constitution ratified by the South Carolina Convention of 1788, which was presided over by Thomas Pinckney. Later Charles Cotesworth was asked by President Washington to become either the Secretary of State or the Secretary of War, or to serve on the Supreme Court of the United States. Eliza was proud that Charles Cotesworth resisted the temptation of these high honors because he felt that his duty at that time lay in South Carolina.

Perhaps the high moment of Eliza's life came on the warm morning in 1791 when she stood beside her daughter, Harriott Horry, on the portico at Hampton to receive George Washington, the first President of the United States. The President waited until Thomas Pinckney had introduced them and stepped aside. Then in his profoundly dignified way, Washington said, "Madam, this is a meeting to which I have long looked forward. As a planter, I pay my respects to you for your early work with indigo and later with silk culture. You are both planter and patriot. Your sons truly reflect your love of principle and their country will soon call them to even greater service. Mothers like you light fires that are never extinguished. As long as that happens, we have nothing to fear for our Republic."

Early the next year, Eliza was to see the President's prediction come true when Washington's appointment of her son Thomas Pinckney as Minister to Great Britain was confirmed. But she was not to live to see Thomas's remarkable diplomatic triumph when, as a special envoy to Spain, he arranged a treaty that established commercial relations between the two countries, settled the boundaries of Spain's territory bordering the United States, and gave the United States freedom to navigate the Mississippi, as well as to use New Orleans as a port of entry. Nor was Eliza to see her other son, Charles Cotesworth, become Minister to France, a major general, and twice Federalist candidate for the Presidency.

Eliza Lucas Pinckney died in Philadelphia on May 26, 1793. Her funeral took place there the next day at St. Peter's Church with President Washington, by his own request, acting as one of the pallbearers. Even in her last illness, Eliza had been willing to dare. She had risked a journey from Charles Town to Philadelphia on the chance that a noted surgeon of that city might enable her to explore life a little longer. To the very end, as Charles Pinckney once said, she had "a lively spirit and a questing mind."

Bibliography

MANUSCRIPT SOURCES

Public Record Office, London
Colonial Office Records, Leeward Islands
Correspondence, Board of Trade: C.O. 152/24, Y 47, 49, 55, 58, 61, 69, 70; C.O. 152/25, Y 74-175, pp. 126, 142, 251.
Correspondence, Secretary of State: C.O. 152/40, 1721-1749; C.O. 152/44, 1734-1745, No. 47; C.O. 152/45, 1748-1752, No. 48.
Books of Commissions, Introductions, Correspondence . . . Board of Trade: C.O. 153/16, 1735 June 18—1747 Dec. 2, pp. 129, 130.
Board of Trade Records: C.O. 326/Ind. 8342, 1703-1729; Ind. 8343, 1729-1743; Ind. 8344, 1744-1759.
America and the West Indies, Antigua 1689 to 1820: C.O. 7/1.
Paper Office: America and West Indies, Leeward Caribee Islands 1734-1745: C.O. 152/44/91, 154, 169-180, 181, 187, 195.
Signet Office Docquet Book, May 1741-December 1748 [Treasury Records], Ind. 6824/October, 1743.

South Carolina Historical Society, Charleston
Letters and journals of Eliza Lucas.

The National Society of Colonial Dames in the State of South Carolina
Receipt [Recipe] Book of Mrs. Eliza Lucas Pinckney.

Charleston Library, Charleston
Letter of George Lucas to Charles Pinckney.

Manuscript Division, Library of Congress, Washington
Letters and papers of the Pinckney family, including letters from

Charles Cotesworth Pinckney and Harriott Pinckney Horry to their mother, Mrs. Eliza Lucas Pinckney, as well as personal expense account books of Charles Pinckney during 1754-1756 portion of his stay in England as agent for South Carolina.

PRINTED SOURCES

Acts of the Privy Council of England, Colonial Series, ed. by W. L. Grant and James Munro, Vol. III, Hereford, 1910.

Appleton's Cyclopaedia of American Biography, 6 vols., Vol. V, New York, 1888.

Antigua and the Antiguans: a full account of the colony and . . . biographical notices of the principal families, 2 vols., London, 1844.

Bemis, Samuel Flagg, *Pinckney's Treaty. America's Advantage from Europe's Distress, 1783-1800,* rev. ed., New Haven and London, 1965.

Bent, Arthur Cleveland, *Life Histories of North American Marsh Birds,* New York, 1963.

Brewster, Ray Q., *Organic Chemistry,* 2nd ed., New York, 1963.

Calendar of State Papers, Colonial Series, America and the West Indies, 1737, ed. by K. G. Davies, Vol. XLIII, London, 1963.

Catesby, Mark, *The Natural History of Carolina, Florida and the Bahama Islands* (1731, 1743, 1748), London, 1771.

Charleston City Gazette and Daily Advertiser, July 17, 1793.

Clowes, William Laird, *The Royal Navy, A History, From Earliest Times to the Present,* 5 vols., Vol. III, London, 1898.

Dalton, George, F.R.G.S., *George the First's Army 1714-1727,* Vols. I and II, London, 1910, 1912.

De Saussure, Mrs. Nancy (Bostick), *Old Plantation Days* . . . , New York, 1909.

Dexter, Elizabeth Anthony, *Colonial Women of Affairs,* Boston and New York, 1931.

Drayton, John, *The Carolinian Florist of Governor John Drayton of South Carolina,* Columbia, S.C., 1943.

English Army Lists and Commission Register (1661-1714), ed. and annot. by Charles Dalton, F.G.R.S., 6 vols., Vols. III and VI, London, 1896, 1904.

Eppes, Susan (Bradford), *The Negro of the Old South* . . . , Macon, Ga., 1941.

Gadsden, Christopher E., *A sermon, preached at St. Philip's Church, August 21, 1825, on the occasion of the decease of Gen. Charles Cotes-*

worth Pinckney, Charleston, 1825.

Garden, Alexander, *Eulogy on General Charles Cotesworth Pinckney, 1746-1825,* Charleston, 1825.

The Gentleman's Magazine: and Historical Chronical, 56 vols., Vols. XI, XII, XIII, XVII, London, 1741, 1742, 1743, 1747.

Glen, James, *A Description of South Carolina,* London, 1761.

Griswold, Frank Gray, *Plantation Days,* Norwood, Mass., 1935.

Harlow, Vincent T., *A History of Barbados 1625-1685,* Oxford, 1926.

Hearn, Lafcadio, *Two Years in the French West Indies,* New York, 1890.

Higham, C. S. S., *The Development of the Leeward Islands . . . ,* Cambridge, 1921.

Hollingsworth, Buckner, *Her Garden Was Her Delight,* New York, 1962.

Irving, John Beaufain, *The South Carolina Jockey Club,* Charleston, S.C., 1857.

Jones, Edward Alfred, *American Members of the Inns of Court,* London, 1924.

Lasteyrie du Saillant, Charles P., comte de, 1759-1849, *A treatise on the culture, preparation, history, and analysis of pastel, or woad . . . indigo etc.,* tr. from the French, Boston, 1816.

Lawson, John, *A New Voyage to Carolina containing the Exact Description and Natural History of the Country,* London, 1709.

Ledyard, John, *Methods for Improving the Manufacture of Indigo,* originally submitted to the consideration of the Carolina planters, Devizes, England, 1776.

A List of the Colonels, Lieutenant Colonels, Majors, Captains, Lieutenants and Ensigns of His Majesty's Forces in the British Establishment, London, 1740.

A List of the General and Field Officers, As they Rank in the Army, of the Officers in the Several Regiments of Horse, Dragoons, and Foot on the British and Irish Establishments, London, 1765.

The London Gazette, November, 1742, through January, 1747.

Longwell, M. R., *America and Women,* Philadelphia, 1962.

Luffman, John, *A Brief Account of the Island of Antigua . . . ,* 2nd ed., London, 1790.

Mackenzie-Grieve, Averil, *The Great Accomplishment,* London, 1953.

McCrady, Edward, *The History of South Carolina under the Royal Government, 1719-1776,* New York, 1899.

Nicholas, Edward, *The Hours and the Ages, A Sequence of Americans,* New York, 1949.

Oliphant, Mrs. Mary C. (Simms), *The South Carolina Reader,* Columbia, S.C., 1927.

Phillips, Ulrick Bonnell, *American Negro Slavery,* New York, 1918.

Pinckney, Mrs. Eliza (Lucas), ed. by Mrs. Harriott Pinckney Holbrook, *Journals and Letters of Eliza Lucas,* Wormsloe, Georgia, 1850.

Pinckney, Rev. Charles Cotesworth, *Life of General Thomas Pinckney,* Boston and New York, 1895.

Pringle, Mrs. Elizabeth Waties (Allston), *A Woman Rice Planter,* New York, 1922.

Ravenel, Harriott Horry, *Eliza Pinckney,* New York, 1896, 1925.

Ravenel, Mrs. St. Julien, *Charleston, the Place and the People,* New York and London, 1922.

Reasons for laying a duty on French and Spanish indigo and granting a bounty on what is made in the British plantations [London ?], 1748.

Reports and Documents of the East India Company In Regard to the Culture and Manufacture of Cotton, Wool, Raw Silk and Indigo, London, 1836,

Rhett, Robert Goodwyn, *Charleston; An Epic of Carolina,* Richmond, Va., 1940.

Riddell, Mrs. Marie Woodley, *A Voyage to the Madeira and Leeward, Caribbean Isles,* London, 1792.

Sellers, Leila, *Charleston Business on the Eve of the American Revolution,* Chapel Hill, N.C., 1934.

Smith, Alice R. Huger, and D. E. Huger Smith, *The Dwelling Houses of Charleston, South Carolina,* Philadelphia and London, 1917.

Smith, Alice Ravenel, and Herbert Ravenel Sass, *A Carolina Rice Planter of the Fifties . . . ,* New York, 1936.

South Carolina Gazette (name varied slightly in some years), 1738-1767.

South Carolina Historical and Genealogical Magazine, April, 1901; October, 1907; January, 1913; January, 1915; April, 1915; July, 1916; January, 1918; October, 1920.

Stoney, Samuel Gaillard, ed. by Albert Simons, F.A.I.A., and Samuel Lapham, Jr., F.A.I.A., *Plantations of the Carolina Low Country,* Charleston, 1938.

Watkins, Frederick Henry, *Handbook of the Leeward Islands,* London, 1924.

Sources of Quoted Material

1. Page 107 (Eliza to brother): Harriott Horry Pinckney, *Eliza Pinckney* (New York: Charles Scribner's Sons, 1896), p. 12.
2. Page 108 (both quotations, Eliza to Mary Bartlett): *ibid.*, pp. 34–35.
3. Page 117 (Eliza to her father): *ibid.*, p. 9.
4. Page 118 (Eliza to her father): *ibid.*, p. 9.
5. Page 127 (Eliza to cousin): *ibid.*, p. 93.
6. Page 128 (first three quotations, Eliza to Mary Bartlett): *ibid.*, p. 38.
   (final quotation, Eliza to Mary Bartlett): *ibid.*, pp. 31–32.
7. Page 130 (Eliza to Mary Bartlett): *ibid.*, p. 31.
8. Pages 130–131 (both quotations, Eliza to Mary Bartlett): *ibid.*, p. 56.
9. Page 137 (Eliza to Mary Bartlett): *ibid.*, pp. 51–52.
10. Pages 139–140 (Eliza to friend): *ibid.*, p. 54.
11. Page 153 (Eliza to her mother): *ibid.*, p. 101.
12. Page 163 (Eliza to unnamed friend in South Carolina): *ibid.*, p. 147.
13. Page 165 (first quotation, Eliza to her mother): *ibid.*, p. 175. (both quotations from will of Charles Pinckney): Rev. Charles Cotesworth Pinckney, D.D., *Life of General Thomas Pinckney* (Boston and New York: Houghton, Mifflin and Company, 1895), p. 21.

Index